PSYCHOSIS AND CIVILIZATION

PSYCHOSIS AND CIVILIZATION

Two Studies in the Frequency of Mental Disease

By

HERBERT GOLDHAMER and ANDREW W. MARSHALL

SOCIAL SCIENCE DIVISION, THE RAND CORPORATION

THE FREE PRESS, GLENCOE, ILLINOIS

CONTENTS

5

/2617

TABLES AND CHARTS

* Arabic numbers designate tables and Roman numerals designate charts.

9

FOREWORD

THE TWO studies presented in this volume complement each other. The first attempts to show, and in fact we believe does show, that there has been no increase in the frequency of the psychoses during the past one hundred years. The second examines in greater detail the frequency of major mental illnesses today and provides a convenient means of expressing this in terms of the risk of such illness during the individual's life span or some particular portion of it.

Looked at from the standpoint of their implications for social welfare, the results of these two studies make a contrasting impression. The first provides a fairly agreeable view of the future, agreeable that is to a generation whose optimism often has to base itself on the conviction that at any rate things are not getting worse. Certainly there is comfort to be gotten from findings that dispel the gloomier expectations concerning the future mental health of the nation. Most of these are based on the belief that there has been, during the past generation, a steady increase in the frequency of the psychoses. This view is here shown to be unwarranted. The satisfaction to be derived from this is, however, somewhat dimmed by the findings of the second study which estimates the probability that a person who survives to a given age will be stricken by a serious mental illness of either an episodic or continuing nature. We have estimated that this chance is about 1 in 20 by the age of 45 and about 1 in 10 by the age of 65. In the light of this we are not likely to be led, by the results of our first study, to indulge in festive celebrations. Our findings give us warrant for emphasizing not that mental health is just as good today as it was in the past, but rather that mental health was just as bad in the past as it is now.

When we speak here about mental health or mental illness we refer to the absence or presence of a psychosis or a mental disturbance of considerable severity, generally hospitalizable. We have not studied the incidence of the neuroses and character disorders. As we point out in our work it is entirely possible that these have been on the increase. We provide some theoretical considerations in terms of which this may be judged in the absence of adequate data permitting direct measurement. Although we discuss mental health primarily in terms of the frank psychoses and neuroses, we recognize that the mental health literature, especially that written by social scientists, shows an increasing tendency to equate mental health with various other terms that convey somewhat broader concerns: adjustment, emotional maturity, happiness, effective living, communal harmony. Desirable as it obviously is, in some contexts, to have such broad terms of reference in discussing mental health, it is unfortunate that this practice sometimes reflects a certain weariness in dealing with the scientific problems raised by those who are just plain sick.

We have called this book *Psychosis and Civilization* because we want to call attention to the scientific and historical problem to which our detailed findings are, after all, intended primarily to apply. What this application is we have discussed in the conclusion of the first study and only in the degree of detail that we feel our data allow. Our analysis of the problem is overshadowed by the detailed presentation of our data and our method of work. For this reason we have thought it useful in the title to draw specific attention to the general problem which motivated these studies and lends special interest to their results.

It is not easy to free oneself from the conviction that the

striking social developments of the past hundred years, with the multiple and often conflicting pressures on the individual that they appear to have brought in their train, have been without effect on the incidence of the psychoses. Some students in this field have pointed out to us that in the mid-19th century Massachusetts was already an urbanized and industrialized area and that the same can be said of Oneida County in New York, these being the two areas from which our trend data are primarily drawn. This is quite true but it precisely concedes the point we have argued, namely that the social changes of the last century, striking as they may seem, have not been sufficient to alter the incidence of the psychoses. To be sure there is an implication, in the type of remark we are commenting on, that had we been able to begin our time series still earlier, say in 1740 instead of 1840, then we would have observed that the early growth of industrialism-urbanism was in fact accompanied by an increase in the psychoses. This is conceivably so. Unfortunately this view is not likely to have to face an empirical test because adequate data for such early periods do not seem to exist. In any case when common assumptions about the 19th century rates are shown to be incorrect, it is scarcely good intellectual practice simply to fall back another century and assume that the alleged increase in the psychoses occurred at that time.

We cannot claim, on the basis of our data, that the incidence of the psychoses prior to 1840 was the same as after that date. Nor are we in a position to argue that the social transformations of the last two or three centuries have left the frequency of the psychoses unaltered. We do, however, think it proper to point out that the constancy of trend data carried back to 1840 suggests the wisdom of modifying or holding in abeyance the common assumptions concerning the impact of social change on the incidence of psychosis.

In this connection our brief statement (p. 76) on mid-19th

century mental hospital admission rates for residents of Fayette County, Kentucky and Davidson County, Tennessee becomes relevant. We believe that these counties had admission rates in the mid-19th century equal to those of Kentucky and Tennessee today. These counties did not in the mid-19th century have the urban-industrial character of 19th century Massachusetts and Oneida County, New York, from which most of our data are drawn. They thus indicate that the constancy of rates to which we refer does not simply apply to those areas which in the 19th century had already taken on many of the urban-industrial characteristics of later years.

Since our work was completed there has come to hand Dr. Kurt H. Fremming's fine study of the frequency of mental illness on the Danish island of Bornholm.* This work, which continues the splendid series of Scandinavian investigations in social psychiatry, has relevance for both of the studies contained in this volume. Bornholm has a population of 46,000, mostly engaged in agriculture and fishing. There are some craftsmen and some industry. The largest town on Bornholm is 11,000, most of the others being considerably smaller. The social and economic level of the island does not differ from the rest of Denmark; there are no great social differences, and no proletariat. Most of the people are characterized as lower middle class. Inbreeding is no greater than in Denmark as a whole. Although one certainly cannot argue that this is a population that has entirely escaped all the developments usually considered characteristic of modern mass society, it is apparent that it retains many of the features considered conducive to a satisfactory mental health level. Dr. Fremming has given us expectancy figures for various classes of mental disorders up to the age of 56. If we include those cases that are comparable to the

---

* Kurt H. Fremming, M.D., "The Expectation of Mental Infirmity in a Sample of the Danish Population," *Occasional Papers on Eugenics,* No. 7, The Eugenics Society and Cassell and Company, Ltd., London, 1951.

classes we consider in our second study, we observe that for this age group risk of a serious mental disorder on Bornholm is just about that which we have calculated for New York state. Evidence has also increased in our own country that points to a parity of urban and rural rates. However much we may believe that the rural scene has been contaminated by the spiritual malaise of modern urban life, this also tends to show that social developments previously considered productive of psychotic breakdowns are by no means as significant as they have been assumed to be.

From comments that we have received it is apparent that to some who have not had an opportunity to examine 19th century mental hospital reports the use of such early material seems a rather hazardous scientific venture. We have today become so professionalized in the procedures of institutional and scientific bookkeeping that we sometimes forget that recording and counting admissions to a hospital, noting dates of entrance, county of residence and such like matters are intellectual operations which even in the 19th century had already been conquered. As for diagnostic accuracy, a problem sufficiently difficult in our own day and unquestionably even less satisfactorily solved in the 19th century, it should be noted that we have not been interested in differentiating the frequency of separate psychoses, but have dealt with them as a total group. This raises only the question whether the class of persons admitted to the 19th century hospitals were psychotics in the contemporary sense of the term. We believe that the evidence we provide on this will satisfy the reader.

We apologize for the large amount of footnote material and the often tedious detail and documentation of our study. We have felt, however, that precisely because questions would undoubtedly arise concerning the validity of materials drawn from non-contemporary sources it was necessary to provide the fullest possibility of checking our sources and our methods of estimation and computation.

* * *

These two studies were completed in 1949 and received a limited distribution as a report prepared for the United States Air Force as a part of the research program of Project RAND administered by The RAND Corporation. We wish to record our indebtedness for the many comments we have received from those who saw this study in its RAND report form. We want to thank more particularly Dr. Margaret Merrell of the School of Hygiene and Public Health of Johns Hopkins University for her valuable criticisms of the second study; Dr. Hans Speier, Chief of the Social Science Division, The RAND Corporation, who read the original manuscript and gave us many thoughtful comments; and Professor W. Allen Wallis, Chairman of the Committee on Statistics, the University of Chicago, for his continued interest in our work.

PART I

*A CENTURY OF
MENTAL HOSPITAL ADMISSION RATES
IN MASSACHUSETTS*

ACKNOWLEDGMENTS

TO THE Library of Congress we are indebted for access to its very fine collection of early Massachusetts mental hospital reports.

To the Public Document Division of the Army Medical Library we are indebted for various state reports and for the procurement of some items not available in Washington.

To those to whom our indebtedness is greatest, mortality debars us from expressing our gratitude: Dr. Pliny Earle (1809–1892) and Dr. Edward Jarvis (1803–1884).

1 *INTRODUCTION*

THE IMMEDIATE AIM of this report is to establish acceptable estimates of age-specific first admission rates to institutions caring for the mentally ill in Massachusetts for the years 1840 to 1885 in order to compare these rates with those of the contemporary period. No antiquarian zeal or historical interest has moved us to engage in this laborious task.[1] Our interest is in providing a more adequate test than is now available of contending views concerning the incidence of the major mental disorders in our own day and in an earlier period. We assume that a more adequate test of these beliefs will throw light on the validity of contentions concerning the psychologically pathic effects of contemporary social existence. To be sure, today it is no longer so readily assumed that there has been a true increase in the incidence of mental disease. This, however, does not seem to have diminished appreciably the conviction that "civilization," with its high degree of individuation, personal insecurity and competitiveness, and its killing "pace," is responsible for a large measure of our psychotic population.[2]

1. Nor were we concerned to show that a judicious use of documents usually reserved for historical study can extend the horizons of comparative statistical social analysis to phenomena other than those of a demographic and economic character. Yet the present study does show that the past is not always as irrecoverable, statistically speaking, as is sometimes assumed.
2. It is possible, of course, that contemporary social life has produced an increase in the incidence of the neuroses but has had an imperceptible effect on the incidence of the major psychoses. In this report we are concerned with the latter category of mental disorders.

2 PROBLEM, SOURCES, AND PROCEDURES

THE RECENT REACTION against earlier claims that mental disorders were on the increase has found support in a number of studies that have attempted to demonstrate that significant changes in mental hospital admission rates have not occurred. These studies suffer from several limitations which give them a diminished evidential character. Most of the studies usually cited in this connection cover too short a time span to dispel the conviction that the major mental diseases are increasing. Elkind and Taylor,[3] although their article is entitled "The Alleged Increase in the Incidence of the Major Psychoses," discuss admission rates for Massachusetts only from 1922–33 and for New York State from 1917–34. Similarly, Jacob,[4] in "A Note on the Alleged Increase in Insanity," deals only with the period 1923–32. Dorn,[5] who is sometimes cited in this connection, covers only a 10-year period (Massachusetts, 1920–30) and Sommer and Harman [6] a 20-year period (Illinois, 1922–34). Such narrow time spans scarcely exclude the possibility that a substantial in-

3. Henry B. Elkind and Maurice Taylor, "The Alleged Increase in the Incidence of the Major Psychoses," *The American Journal of Psychiatry*, XCII (1936), pp. 817-25.
4. J. S. Jacob, "A Note on the Alleged Increase of Insanity," *Journal of Abnormal and Social Psychology*, XXIII (1938), pp. 390-97.
5. Harold F. Dorn, "The Incidence and Future Expectancy of Mental Disease," United States Public Health Service, *Public Health Reports*, LIII, No. 45 (1938), pp. 1991-2004.
6. Conrad Sommer and Harry H. Harman, "Trends in Mental Diseases in Illinois, 1922–43," in American Psychopathological Association, *Trends of Mental Disease* (New York, King's Crown Press, 1945), pp. 56-91.

crease in hospital admission rates might be revealed if these time series began at a considerably earlier date. Winston,[7] under the title "The Assumed Increase of Mental Disease," discusses admission rates for New York State from 1909–30 and for Massachusetts from 1904–30. She concludes that there is no evidence of a true increase in the incidence of mental disease in these states. Malzberg,[8] whose work for New York State covers approximately the same period, concludes that there has been a significant upward trend in rates and vigorously contends that this is due to an actual increase in the incidence of mental disease. The longest single series available is provided by Elkind's [9] first study which pushed the time series back into the 19th century and presented first admission rates for Massachusetts beginning with 1881. These rates show an increase of approximately 60 percent between 1881 and 1912, and a stabilization of the rates after the latter year. Elkind attributes the increase between 1881 and 1912 to differences in the facilities available and to a changed attitude toward seeking treatment in mental hospitals. Although this interpretation is not without plausibility, the need to explain away in this fashion, for so relatively late a period, an increase of such considerable magnitude scarcely gives support to the hypothesis that no increase in the actual incidence of mental disease has occurred in the years under analysis.[10]

A second limitation of a number of the studies in this field is

7. Ellen Winston, "The Assumed Increase of Mental Disease," *American Journal of Sociology*, XL (1935), pp. 427-39.

8. Benjamin Malzberg, *Social and Biological Aspects of Mental Disease* (Utica, State Hospitals Press, 1940), pp. 38-51.

9. Henry B. Elkind, "The Epidemiology of Mental Disease: A Preliminary Discussion," *American Journal of Psychiatry*, VI (1927), pp. 623-40.

10. We shall, in fact, show that while differences in hospital facilities are very important earlier in the 19th century in accounting for smaller rates, during the years 1880–85 age-specific admission rates for the central age groups were just as high as today. Consequently, for these ages there is no difference to be "explained away."

their failure to provide age-specific rates,[11] or even rates adequately adjusted for age changes in the population. Elkind's 1881–1925 series is simply calculated on a total population base. A number of other studies rely on an "adjustment for age" that involves computing rates for the population 15 years of age and over. This adjustment is too gross to handle adequately changes in the age structure of the population.[12] Further, we shall show that there have also been, since the 19th century, marked changes, *independent of population shifts,* in the age pattern of admissions. We must, therefore, suppose that the relation between earlier and contemporary rates varies considerably from age group to age group. *Standardization of rates for age does not take account of this.* Only age-specific admission rates are capable of showing the true nature of any change or lack of change that has occurred.

Because of the limitations of present studies with respect to time period covered and the non-age-specific character of many of the rates provided, we undertook to construct a new series that would begin with 1840 and provide age-specific first admission rates. Massachusetts was chosen as the state of inquiry because its facilities for the care of the mentally ill during the last half of the 19th century were, despite their obvious limitations, more advanced than those of most other states.[13] The relatively small size of Massachusetts is also favorable to our inquiry, since

11. This does not apply to Malzberg's study cited above, which does supply age-specific rates, nor to Dayton's analysis of Massachusetts rates from 1917–40 in Public Health Reports, Suppl. No. 168, *Mental Health in Later Maturity* (Washington, 1943), pp. 112-17. Dayton and Malzberg come to opposite conclusions.

12. Thus Elkind (*op. cit.,* 1936) finds an increase of 4 percent between 1920 and 1930 in the Massachusetts manic-depressive rate. These rates were calculated on the population 15 years of age and over. When, however, we calculate the rates based on the cases and the corresponding population in the age group 20 to 54, the increase becomes 8 percent. We do not point this out in order to contend that there has been a true increase in this 10-year period in the incidence of manic-depressive psychoses, but simply to show that arguments based on rates inadequately adjusted for age are not acceptable.

13. The following opinions are typical of other expressions to be found in

it diminishes the mean distance of the population from a mental hospital. It has been well known for some time now that the tendency, especially in the past, to hospitalize the mentally ill is inverse to their distance from a mental hospital. Massachusetts further recommends itself for study during the latter half of the 19th century because of the work of such leaders in institutional psychiatry as Dr. Edward Jarvis and Dr. Pliny Earle. Their studies and reports, together with the documents and reports of official state agencies and hospitals, made feasible an investigation which one might have supposed quite impossible at this late date.

It is not to be denied that even the presentation of *first* admission rates for so early a period is in itself a novelty and that the attempt to carry this to a further stage of refinement by calculating *age-specific* first admission rates may seem extremely hazardous. However, we shall present quite fully the sources of our data and all assumptions involved in their utilization. The reader will be in a position to judge for himself whether any of our assumptions were or were not warranted. We turn now to various questions concerning our data which the reader will wish answered.

Institutional Coverage

The first column of Table 1, which summarizes first admissions from 1840 to 1885, lists the institutions that our survey

---

the contemporary literature: "Probably no other State in the Union expends so much for its insane, in proportion to its population, as Massachusetts does." (F. B. Sanborn, *The Public Charities of Massachusetts During the Century Ending January 1, 1876: A Report Made to the Massachusetts Centennial Commission, February 1, 1876* (Boston, 1876), p. 53.) "There are few if any other States so well supplied with [mental] hospitals as Massachusetts." (Pliny Earle, M.D., *Psychologic Medicine: Its Importance as a Part of the Medical Curriculum: An Address Delivered Before the Berkshire Medical Institute, November 24, 1863* (Utica, 1867), p. 13.)

has covered. They fall into five groups: Massachusetts state mental hospitals, state almshouses, county receptacles for the insane, town almshouses, and private hospitals. The state hospitals received privately paying patients and state and town paupers, that is, persons whose keep was paid for by the state and towns. The three state almshouses received state insane paupers. The receptacles for the insane were intended as county institutions; by a law of 1836 each county in the state was supposed to provide such a receptacle attached to its house of correction. In actual fact, however, the only three receptacles provided were at South Boston, Ipswich, and Cambridge. In 1864 there were in Massachusetts 216 town almshouses.[14] As in the case of the state almshouses only a minority of their residents were insane, and it is only the latter, of course, that we deal with in the admissions presented in Table 1. The only major private hospital operating throughout our period was the McLean Hospital in Boston; this was the psychiatric branch of the Massachusetts General Hospital. "Its patients are not the poor, but, in a great degree, the rich." [15] This hospital also received some charity patients. Beginning with 1870, our table shows a small number of admissions from other private hospitals. We know that there were two or three private mental "hospitals" in earlier years, but the number of patients (about 25) that they housed at that time is negligible. Since we were unable to secure further data, we have no entries prior to 1870 for this class of small private hospitals. For the town almshouses we were not able to secure adequate data on admissions or number of resident patients for the decade 1840–49. In the period 1850–54 this group constituted 9 percent of all other admissions. The reader is free to extrapolate this percentage

14. *First Annual Report of the [Massachusetts] Board of State Charities, January, 1865,* Public Document No. 19 (Boston, 1865).
15. *First Annual Report of the State Board of Health, Lunacy, and Charity, 1879,* Public Document No. 17 (Boston, 1880), p. xxii.

TABLE 1

NUMBER OF FIRST ADMISSIONS TO INSTITUTIONS CARING FOR
THE INSANE, MASSACHUSETTS, BY 5-YEAR PERIODS, 1840 TO 1884,
AND 1885

INSTITUTIONS	1840–1844	1845–1849	1850–1854	1855–1859	1860–1864	1865–1869	1870–1874	1875–1879	1880–1884	1885
1. McLean	428	445	422	413	300	280	241	234	234	6
2. South Boston	148	223	342	260	314	246	174	144	368	9
3. Worcester	734	912	951	799	707	917	1352	1044	777	22.
4. Taunton	(*)	(*)	91	764	836	876	1479	1573	964	21
5. Northampton	(*)	(*)	(*)	69	273	370	410	334	460	9
6. Danvers	(*)	(*)	(*)	(*)	(*)	(*)	(*)	798	1915	38
7. Ipswich and Cambridge	120	140	170	100	80	62	68	80	30	
8. Tewksbury	(*)	(*)	(*)	42	18	100	81	112	71	1
9. Small Private Hospitals	(*)	(*)	(†)	(†)	(†)	(†)	14	85	168	4
10. Town Almshouses, Bridgewater, Monson, Prisons	(148)	(188)	194	194	164	91	218	443	386	8
11. TOTAL	1578	1908	2170	2641	2692	2942	4037	4847	5373	120
12. Percent of first admissions based on exact enumerations of first and/ or total admissions	83.0	82.9	83.2	87.3	90.4	91.4	94.5	91.0	92.9	93.
13. Rate per 100,000 general population	39.4	41.1	40.8	44.6	43.1	43.2	51.9	56.3	57.8	62.
14. Massachusetts 1940 first admission rate (107) standardized for age at decennial intervals		85.2		84.8		87.9		91.3		

* Hospital or other institution did not exist or regularly receive mental patients during the indicated period.

† Adequate information not available (see text, p. 27).

Line 1—McLean Hospital, Boston, a private mental hospital. Exact number of first admissions and total admissions available from reports for 1868–85. For 1840–67 only total admissions available. The ratio of first to total admissions during 1868–85 (.70) used to estimate first admissions from total admissions for 1840–67. First admissions with out-of-state residence eliminated (see text, p. 34).

Line 2—South Boston Hospital, originally a Suffolk county "receptacle for the insane." First admissions available for 1868–85 from annual reports of the Board of State Charities and the State Board of Health, Lunacy, and Charity. These years provide a first-to-total-admission ratio of .75. This ratio has been back to the preceding decade. During this first decade of our series it is also likely that a certain number of insane in houses of correction and in prisons and jails are omitted. After 1855 the use of such institutions for the confinement of the non-criminal insane virtually ceased in Massachusetts.

---

used for the years 1840–67 for which only total admissions were directly available from the hospital reports. This ratio is in agreement with that of Worcester (the only other nonprivate major hospital) whose first-to-total-admission ratio is directly known for these years.

Line 3—State hospital. Opened 1832. First admissions directly available, 1840–85, in official reports.

Line 4—State hospital. Opened 1854. First admissions directly available from official reports.

Line 5—State hospital. Opened 1858. First admissions directly available from official reports. First admissions with out-of-state residence eliminated (see text, p. 34).

Line 6—State hospital. Opened 1878. First admissions directly available from official reports.

Line 7—County receptacles. After 1855 the admission figures refer only to Ipswich, as Cambridge closed shortly after 1854. For the period 1840–54 we have estimated first admissions from an exact count of resident insane given in *Report on Insanity and Idiocy in Massachusetts, by the Commission on Lunacy, Under Resolve of the Legislature of 1854*, Public Document No. 144 (1855); and in Massachusetts enumeration of insane in institutions in the Massachusetts state census of 1855. For these years we assume that the proportion Ipswich and Cambridge contribute to first admissions is the same as the proportion that they contribute to the total number of insane in institutions (8.9 percent). For the years 1868–85 first and total admissions were directly available from the reports of the State Board of Health, Lunacy, and Charity. These gave a first-to-total-admission ratio of .62, and this ratio was used to estimate first admissions for 1865–67 for which only total admissions were available. First admissions for 1855–64 are interpolations from the 1850–54 and 1865–69 first admissions.

Line 8—A state almshouse, opened in 1854. Exact figures on first admissions of the insane available for 1868–85. For 1854–67 we have total admissions minus transfers from state hospitals giving virtually exact first admissions.

Line 9—See text, p. 27.

Line 10—This line is a residual of all other classes of institutionalized insanity. The major group is comprised of those in town almshouses; the rest are composed of insane in Bridgewater, Monson (originally state almshouses), prisons, and a few cases contracted out, under supervision of the Overseers of the Poor, to the care of private families. For this line we had prevalency figures available, the first of any real value being for the year 1854 (Public Document No. 144, cited under note to Line 7 above). We have used enumerations of the resident insane in the almshouses to arrive at first admission rates. On the basis of evidence in the First Annual Report of the Board of State Charities (1865) we have thrown out 60 percent of the prevalency cases as being persons formerly in other mental institutions. We have also eliminated 15 percent of the remainder as representing persons who may have been admitted later from town

First Admissions

Although it is true that the routine use of first admissions in the calculation of incidence rates is a relatively late development, recognition of the importance of segregating first and subsequent admissions is older than is perhaps realized. This distinction, with a full awareness of its significance, is already found in Dr. Pliny Earle's *History, Description and Statistics of the Bloomingdale Asylum for the Insane* published in 1848. Later, in 1869, as superintendent of the Massachusetts State Lunatic Hospital at Northampton, he began the practice of enumerating first and readmissions separately. At the same time, at the request of the secretary of the Massachusetts Board of State Charities, each state hospital began to report patients to the Board according to whether they had never been in any hospital; were former patients at that particular hospital; were former patients of other hospitals in Massachusetts, of hospitals in other states, and of hospitals in other countries. Fortunately the state hospitals went back to their original registers and segregated first and readmissions for all the years since their founding. We thus have, for the four state hospitals in opera-

---

almshouses to other hospitals. (This was done because transfers from town almshouses were not treated by state hospitals as readmissions.) The 15-percent elimination is based on data from which we have computed the probability that a person admitted to one hospital and later discharged will be readmitted to a different hospital. After these eliminations we assumed that the remaining prevalency cases represented the same contribution of first admissions relative to prevalency as is true for the rest of the state.

From 1864–85 sufficient prevalency data were available for our purposes in this residual line. For 1854 we have a very satisfactory prevalency count(see above). 1855–63 is essentially interpolation from the aforementioned data. We secured no data for 1840–49 that we felt were useable. We have provided in parentheses an extrapolation backwards from the data for 1850–54. Since these miscellaneous forms of institutionalization appear to have played even a larger role in the earliest years when facilities were much less well developed, the reader can use the entries in parentheses without too much hesitation.

Line 12—See text, p. 31.

tion during our period, first admissions for the entire period 1840–85. For the South Boston and McLean Hospitals, first admission data were available only for the latter part of our period. But we were able, on the basis of total admission data which are available in the annual reports from 1840 on, to make good estimates of the proportion of first admissions in these earlier years. For the smaller institutions we met greater difficulty in securing first admission data, and estimates based on the number of resident insane, together with some total admission data, sometimes involving interpolation, had to be made. The notes to Table 1 indicate the procedures we have followed wherever estimates have been made.

The reader who examines in detail the notes to Table 1, with their sometimes rather complicated account of various corrections and estimates for the smaller institutions, may possibly arrive at the impression that our first admission totals in Table 1 rest on an insubstantial foundation. It should, therefore, be pointed out that for most of the 5-year periods the proportion of all admissions for which we have exact or virtually exact data in official reports is over 90 percent.[16] Line 12 of Table 1 gives the proportion for each 5-year period. It should be added that the 10 percent of admissions based on estimates are derived from assumptions that in all cases are conservative. It is virtually certain that any error in our estimates is an error of underenumeration and not overenumeration.

As for the general accuracy of the admission bookkeeping

16. In giving the proportion of first admissions based on "exact" information, we have included not only the large group in which this is strictly the case, but also the smaller number of first admissions estimated from exact total admission data. We have such an abundance of data on the ratio of first to total admissions and these show such complete stability that it would only be misleading to include these latter cases in the category of estimated first admissions. The 10 percent of cases that we count as estimated (in the sense of Line 12, Table 1) involve more serious, though nonetheless very conservative, assumptions.

and reporting of the hospital and state reports of this period, we can only say that intensive reading, analysis, and cross-checking of them have given us the highest esteem for the thoroughness and integrity of the hospital admission data they present. The system of financial accounting for the support of state and town paupers and for receipts from privately paying patients made accurate records imperative. In the earlier years especially, the hospital "paper work" was looked after by the medical superintendent himself. One is impressed by the almost obsessive detail and thoroughness of the statistical summaries of some of the reporters. In a number of respects the early Massachusetts hospital reports are more illuminating than those produced today.

Age Distribution of First Admissions

In order to arrive at age-specific first admission rates we required the age distribution of patients admitted for the first time to an institution. For the entire period, 1840 to 1885, wherever first admission data were not available it was possible to secure from the official reports of the state mental hospitals the age distribution of their *total* admissions. For the South Boston Hospital we were able to secure the age distribution of total admissions only for the years 1850–54 and 1860–64. The age distribution for these two periods was very close to that provided by the state hospital reports for the corresponding years; we have assumed that the age distribution of the South Boston admissions for the remaining years in our series is likewise similar to that of the other hospitals.[17] For the McLean

17. Using six age intervals, the age distributions of total admissions for South Boston and the remainder of the state give $X^2 = 6.74$. For five degrees of freedom this gives $P = .23$; that is, the difference between Boston Hospital and the rest of the state could be expected to occur simply on a sampling basis about once in four times even though the true difference were zero.

Hospital we were not able to secure the age distribution of total admissions until 1876. This age distribution was virtually identical with that of the rest of the state and hence we have used the total state age distribution for McLean in the earlier years as well.

What we required, of course, was the age distribution of *first* admissions rather than total admissions. Here, however, we were able to secure only scattered evidence primarily supplied by Dr. Earle in his Northampton reports. They provided, for several years, the age distribution of first admissions. This differed so little from the age distribution of total admissions that the use of the total admissions age distribution gave us a fully satisfactory basis for the calculation of age-specific first admission rates.[18] It should also be pointed out that in the period we are considering 65 to 75 percent of total admissions were first admissions. Consequently the age distribution of total admissions is in any case considerably weighted by first admissions. The final piece of evidence bearing on the use of the total admission age distribution for first admissions is provided by direct data on the age distribution of first admissions for 1880–85. This period in Table 1 is based on the exact reporting of the age distribution of first admissions. We found that the assumptions we had used in the earlier years gave us an extremely striking continuity with the age distribution in this last period where direct evidence is available. Our method of estimation is therefore such that had we applied it to the pe-

18. It might be supposed that the average age of readmissions would normally be higher than the average age of first admissions. This is not, in fact, the case. Thus, during the contemporary period, both Illinois and Massachusetts show a *lower* age for readmissions than for first admissions. This is because patients with the psychoses of the senium are much less likely to be discharged and hence to be readmitted than are patients who enter a hospital at an earlier age. In the 19th century, readmissions do not show a younger age of admission than first admissions because in this period (as we shall show shortly) admissions in the older age groups form a very much lower proportion of admissions than is the case today.

riod 1880–85 we would have come out with an age distribution that is virtually identical with that provided by the official reports.

Residential Status of Patients

Two hospitals in Massachusetts received an appreciable number of out-of-state residents. These were McLean Hospital in Boston, and Northampton Hospital up to the year 1870, after which no out-of-state patients were admitted. The Northampton reports give the residence status of first admissions, and we have eliminated from them all those which are out-of-state, For McLean we have residence data for 1854, 1866, and 1876–85; these show substantial agreement in the proportion of out-of-state patients. We thus eliminated 16 per cent of the first admissions at McLean (1840–85) and 33 percent (1855–64) and 16 percent (1865–69) at Northampton. It might be supposed that the admission of out-of-state residents to Massachusetts institutions was offset by the admission of Massachusetts residents to out-of-state hospitals. Reports from the latter half of our period reveal, however, that the number of Massachusetts residents in out-of-state hospitals amounted to only about 30 persons. This means, of course, a still lower number of first admissions. These are, in any case, offset by a small number of out-of-state patients in the small Massachusetts private hospitals. These were not eliminated in our totals.

Population Base

In calculating our rates we have used both Federal and Massachusetts censuses. This gave us population enumerations at 5-year intervals. Although population enumeration was probably less accurate in the 19th century than today, the difference in the amount of error can hardly be such as to affect, to any appreciable degree, comparisons between the earlier and contemporary period.

The Psychiatric Character of 19th Century Mental Patients

In comparing rates for the institutional population of the period 1840–85 with those of today, the question arises whether those who were admitted as insane in the earlier period correspond to the types of persons received at mental hospitals today. There would be little point in constructing rates for the 19th century if we did not know to what the rates referred, or more particularly, were we not confident that the 19th century and contemporary rates refer to substantially the same phenomenon. We cannot hope, of course, to determine the psychiatric character of the institutional population in our 19th-century period in terms of the diagnostic categories used by mental hospitals today. But it will, in any case, suffice for our purpose if we can establish that the great majority of the patients in the 19th century period were cases of true psychoses in the contemporary sense of the term. For the period with which we deal there is a substantial amount of descriptive material on the patients admitted to the various institutions and a certain amount of statistical data using the then prevailing diagnostic terminology derived largely from Pinel and Esquirol. A first and major question that arises is whether an appreciable number of the patients in the period we study may not have been simple mental defectives without psychoses, and epileptics and alcoholics without psychosis.

The psychiatric literature of this period and the official documents draw a sharp distinction between the dementia of insanity and the amentia of the mentally defective. Thus, Dr. Jarvis writing in 1855 says: "In making this inquiry, the witnesses were especially requested to regard the scientific and recognized distinction between lunatics and idiots. . . . An idiot is one who was originally destitute of mind, or in whom the mental faculties have not been developed. Those who once had the use of their mental faculties, but have lost them through the process of disease, are not idiots, but demented. . . ."[19] The impropriety of keeping mentally defective persons in institutions for the insane is sufficiently clearly recognized to lead to comment indicating the occasional presence in the institutional population of such persons. A summary of the patients admitted to Northampton Hospital during the first 12 years of its operation (1858–70) mentions that three of the 1074 first admissions for these years were mental defectives and not insane.[20] Reports from other hospitals also indicate a low percentage of recognized defectives among the insane. Thus the Twenty-seventh Annual Report for the Worcester Hospital (1859) states that there were three admissions for idiocy of the 200 admissions of that year. For the years 1880–85, 94 cases of idiocy and imbecility are reported among the admissions to the six major Massachusetts mental hospitals; these constitute 1.2 percent of admissions.[21] The proportion of mental defectives without psychosis among first admissions to contemporary Massachusetts mental hospitals is 2.3 percent.[22]

Only a small proportion of admissions during this period

19. *Report on Insanity and Idiocy in Massachusetts by the Commission on Lunacy, Under Resolve of the Legislature of 1854,* Public Document No. 144 (Boston, 1855), p. 79.

20. Pliny Earle, A.M., M.D., Superintendent of the Hospital, *Statistics of the State Lunatic Hospital at Northampton, Mass., to Sept. 30, 1870,* supplement to *Seventeenth Annual Report of the Trustees of the State Lunatic Hospital at Northampton,* Public Document No. 21 (Boston, 1873).

21. *Seventh Annual Report of the State Board of Health, Lunacy, and Charity of Massachusetts,* Public Document No. 17 (Boston, 1886), p. 86.

22. Neil A. Dayton, *New Facts on Mental Disorders* (Springfield, Charles C. Thomas, 1940), p. 466.

were for alcoholism without psychosis. Of the 1074 first admissions to Northampton (1858–70), 31 were admitted for dipsomania and another 8 for delirium tremens. Dr. Earle points out that such patients ought not to be admitted to hospitals for the insane. In the Fifth Annual Report of the Worcester Hospital we read that the number of cases of delirium tremens did not exceed a half dozen during the first 5 years of the hospital's operation. We also learn from the Seventh Annual Report of the same hospital that the attribution of intemperance in the causation of a certain proportion of cases does not signify that these are simple cases of alcoholism. "The form of insanity which, in the Hospital, has been produced by intemperance, is not delirium tremens, but a permanent mania, after that disease has repeatedly occurred. . . ." [23] The previously cited summary of admissions to the six major hospitals for 1880–85 shows less than 1 percent of admissions for alcoholism without psychosis, and slightly over 3 percent for alcoholic insanity.[24] The corresponding figures for contemporary Massachusetts first admissions are 1.0 and 8.1 percent respectively.[25]

Epileptics likewise constitute a very small proportion of the patients during this period. At the Bloomingdale Lunatic

23. *Seventh Annual Report of the Trustees of the State Lunatic Hospital at Worcester* (Boston, 1840), p. 75.

24. That alcoholism was, nonetheless, a social problem of some considerable magnitude is indicated by the opening of a Home for Inebriates in 1857. During its first 7 years, 1857–64, this institution treated 1632 male patients; they had an average residence of 24 days. The principal form of therapy was to provide these patients with sympathy and understanding, to remove feelings of guilt and shame, and to surround them with all the amenities of a refined and gentlemanly clublike existence (minus the bar). The secretary of the Massachusetts Board of State Charities believed that this form of care was very effective. See *First Annual Report of the [Massachusetts] Board of State Charities, January, 1865*, Public Document No. 19 (Boston, 1865), pp. 309-11. Dr. Pliny Earle, on the other hand, speaking of the inebriates who had been in the Northampton Hospital states: "The number who have subsequently wholly abstained from intoxicating drink could be readily counted upon the fingers of one hand, with the thumb and perhaps a finger or two to spare." (*19th Annual Report*, Northampton Hospital, 1875, p. 22.)

25. Dayton, *op. cit.,* pp. 464, 466.

Asylum in New York City we read that of the 1700 cases admitted up to 1848, 2 percent were epileptics. During the first 5 years of operation of the Worcester State Hospital in Massachusetts, 24 of the 643 patients received up to that time are said to have been epileptic. This number includes those admitted in the fifth year of which the report says, "During the last year, we have had an unusual number of Epileptics in the Hospital." [26] In describing the epileptics, it is made clear that a considerable but indeterminate proportion of them were cases of psychosis with epilepsy. In the Twenty-seventh Annual Report of the same hospital for the year 1859, 13 of the 200 patients admitted that year are described as having epilepsy, but all of these are classified as psychosis with epilepsy. Of admissions to the six major mental hospitals of Masaschusetts during 1880–85, 4.6 percent were epileptic. What proportion of these is considered to be psychosis with epilepsy is not stated. This figure compares with 5.3 percent for contemporary Massachusetts mental hospitals, 3.0 percent being with psychosis and 2.3 percent without.[27]

So far we have proceeded by attempting to show that the proportion of patients explicitly recognized as being nonpsychotic among the admissions in the earlier period is extremely small, in fact much smaller than the proportion of nonpsychotics admitted to the mental hospitals of Massachusetts today. The question now arises, however, whether the great bulk of patients who were claimed to be explicitly psychotic were in fact so. It is our conviction that this is indeed the case, and that

26. *Fifth Annual Report of the Trustees of the State Lunatic Hospital at Worcester,* Senate Document No. 5 (Boston, 1883), p. 53.
27. Dayton, *op. cit.,* pp. 464, 466. In this connection it may be added that the view held by some investigators that epilepsy and schizophrenia are inversely associated is disputed by recent studies. See A. Yde, E. Lohse, and A. Faurbye, "On the Relation Between Schizophrenia, Epilepsy, and Induced Convulsions," *Acta Psychiatrica,* Vol. XVI (1941); and P. H. Hock, "Clinical and Biological Interrelations Between Schizophrenia and Epilepsy," *American Journal of Psychiatry,* Vol. XCIX (1943).

the admissions to the mental institutions of the 19th-century period with which we deal represent a *higher* proportion of severe mental derangement and of the functional psychoses than is the case today. It would be difficult to provide the reader with an opportunity to arrive at a similar conviction without a lengthy reproduction of the various descriptions of patients and other indications in which the literature and hospital reports of this period abound. We will, however, review briefly some of the considerations that are relevant here. It should first be pointed out that the very limited facilities for the care of the mentally ill in the 19th century as compared with our own day almost necessarily led to a selectivity of admissions whereby the degree of severity of mental disorder required for admission was greater then than today. This principle of selection was in fact embodied in law, and in the early part of our period we find that admissions to Worcester State Hospital, which, during the first decade of our period account for 50 percent of our first admissions, were by law restricted "to the violent and furious." [28] To be sure, the treatment of the insane prior to hospitalization often provoked the violence and fury that is so frequently stressed in the account of hospitalized patients; after hospitalization, with its much greater freedom of movement and improved care, many of these violent patients are described as becoming relatively peaceful and co-operative. Later, in 1877, when hospital facilities had increased considerably, we read that the pressure of applications still necessitated giving preference in admission to the severer cases.[29]

In reading the descriptive accounts of the patients admitted to hospitals and of their behavior prior to admission and in the

---

28. *Fourth Annual Report of the Trustees of the State Lunatic Hospital at Worcester* (Boston, 1836), p. 160.

29. Charles F. Folsom, "Diseases of the Mind," in *Eighth Annual Report of the State Board of Health of Massachusetts*, Public Document No. 30 (Boston, 1877), p. 361.

hospital, one is rather forcibly struck by their propensity toward denudative, homicidal, suicidal, and coprophiliac activities. Dr. Samuel B. Woodward, the first superintendent of the Worcester Hospital, in summarizing the first thousand admissions to the hospital, classifies 54 percent as mania, 31 percent as melancholia, 15 percent as dementia, and less than 1 percent as idiocy.[30] Speaking of those classified as mania,[31] Dr. Woodward points out that "it is in consequence of the law regulating the Hospital, restricting its admissions to the violent and furious, that so large a proportion of our inmates are of this class."[32] More than half of those manifesting monomania and

30. *Seventh Annual Report of the Trustees of the State Lunatic Hospital at Worcester* (Boston, 1840), p. 41.

31. Some indication of the psychiatric phenomena referred to by mid-19th-century nosology is provided by the following definitions: "All cases of insanity that are active, in which the individual is prone to open violence and outrage, in which the animal feelings impel to excitement, turbulence and noise, are denominated mania, and yet many such reason correctly upon most subjects, and are often insane upon one only. All cases of depression, lowness of spirits, gloomy apprehensions, agitation and alarm, which are attended by uniform dejection, are classed . . . as melancholy. . . . Dementia is more easily defined. In this form of insanity, the whole brain is torpid and the mind dull . . . the physical energies are as much blunted as the mental powers; the whole system is prostrated, and the mind *seems* to be nearly obliterated." *(Seventh Annual Report . . . Worcester* (Boston, 1840), pp. 71-72.

32. *Fourth Annual Report of the Trustees of the State Lunatic Hospital at Worcester* (Boston, 1837), pp. 159-60. This law, however, does not account for the impression among psychiatrists, even later in our period, that insanity is especially "virulent" in New England. The following quotation is of interest: "And here, in passing, I wish to put myself on record as believing in a New England type of insanity, certainly more positive, clearer cut, and less easily managed, than the majority of cases elsewhere. With experience in two New England hospitals, as well as the observation of a large number of the insane from different sections in another latitude, I should still hesitate to put forward this opinion, had I not found it to be confirmed by others who have had equal or greater opportunities than my own for testing its truth or falsity. It may be a trace of the old Puritan blood, but I think, rather, that it is due to the character of our climate, as it soon appears in our foreign population. It is characterized by intensity, . . . the crash of glass is music in its ears; it rends its garments, refuses food so as often to require the stomach-tube, settles into despair so deep that it would seem dementia were it not so actively suicidal, and, in acute cases, dies of maniacal exhaustion out of all proportion to that recorded elsewhere. Of course there is no one at all conversant with

melancholia are said to exhibit a propensity to homicide or suicide. The presence among the patients of a very considerable number of what we today would probably classify as manic-depressive psychoses is indicated by the following: "There is something very interesting in this subject of periodical insanity which is as inexplicable as it is curious." Dr. Woodward then goes on to describe the alternation of periods of violence, rage, and excitement with periods of quiescence, and concludes that at least 10 percent of the hospital patients manifest, in their insanity, "a distinct and marked periodical character." [33] In 1859, of the 200 patients admitted to Worcester, 16 are classified as "monomania of suspicion." [34] We may take it that these comprise various psychoses with paranoid conditions.

In the same year we find the diagnosis of psychosis associated with general paresis in seven of the 200 cases. The accuracy of this diagnosis is suggested by statements to the effect that such cases, unlike those in the other diagnostic categories, never show a recovery. Later in our period, during the years 1880–85, we find that 5.9 percent of admissions to the six major hospitals of the state are classified as paretic. This compares with a figure of 6.1 percent of first admissions for the contemporary period in Massachusetts.[35]

We have dealt at some little length with the psychiatric character of the 19th century patients because this matter will become of some importance when we make our comparisons between 19th and 20th century admission rates. In summary it should be pointed out that today in Massachusetts 22.2 per

---

insanity in any region but sees just such cases as I have outlined; but in New England this seems to be the prevailing type in acute cases, certainly enough so to characterize the section." (Dr. W. W. Godding, superintendent of Taunton Hospital, in *Twenty-third Annual Report . . . Taunton* (Boston, 1877), pp. 24-25.)

33. *Fifth Annual Report . . . Worcester* (Boston, 1838), p. 48.
34. *Twenty-seventh Annual Report . . . Worcester* (Boston, 1859), p. 16.
35. Dayton, *op. cit.*, p. 464.

cent of all first admissions are for nonpsychotic conditions.[36] We estimate that even at the termination of our 19th century period, 1880–85, when the severity of selective standards had been somewhat reduced, only 5-8 percent of admissions were for nonpsychotic conditions.[37] Certainly it is clear that the great majority of the patients in the 19th century Massachusetts institutions were definitely persons who would be admissible to mental hospitals today. We are not suggesting, of course, that the diagnostic categories of the older period are to be equated with the classifications in use today. But the manifest character of psychotic behavior, such as extreme agitation, excitement, deep depression, delusions, hallucinations, suicidal and homicidal acts, are sufficiently recognizable as insanity, irrespective of the classificatory terminology that is used. That today we may look with an air, probably unjustified, of amused superiority at the diagnostic terms of the older period certainly does not argue against the patients, so described, being psychotic in the contemporary sense of the term.[38]

The contemporary emphasis on the arbitrary character of psychiatric nosology and on the underlying unity of diverse symptomatology is not unique to our own day. Dr. Woodward writes: "In truth, insanity is a unit, undefinable, but

36. For males the figure is 25.5 percent and for females 17.9 percent. Calculated from data in the *Annual Report of the Commissioner of Mental Health for the Year Ending November 30, 1939,* Commonwealth of Massachusetts, Public Document No. 117 (1940).

37. This group is made up of 59 cases of delirium tremens, about 160 epileptics without psychosis, 94 mental defectives, 5 opium addicts, 2 neurasthenics, 8 cases of "moral insanity" and 68 classified simply as "not insane." The total number of admissions during these years was 8,079. (The 160 epileptics without psychosis is estimated on the basis of a total of 373 epileptics divided into those with and without psychosis in the proportion current in Massachusetts in 1917–33.) To the evidence from Massachusetts may be added the following: A survey of 11,831 patients admitted to the New York State Hospital at Utica during the years 1843–75 reported only 1.5 percent of these patients as not insane. Charges that sane persons were being confined at the hospital at Dixmont, Pennsylvania, led to a review of 2,981 consecutive admissions, and this survey reported that less than a dozen, made up of dipsomaniacs and opium-eaters, were not insane. (Cf. Charles F. Folsom, *op. cit.,* p. 407.)

easily recognized by those who have watched its every varying appearance. In strongly marked cases, it is easily distinguished, but in those not always easily classified. The symptoms often amalgamate and as often change, so that what is mania today may appear to be melancholy another day." And Dr. Choate writes: "There is a pretty large number which partake so strongly of the characteristics of more than one type of disease, that classification with them is rather an arbitrary matter." [38]

38. *Seventh Annual Report . . . Worcester* (Boston, 1840), p. 72 and *Eleventh Annual Report . . . Taunton* (Boston, 1865), p. 26.

3 COMPARISON OF 19th CENTURY AND CON-
TEMPORARY FIRST ADMISSION RATES

WE NOW TURN to an analysis of our findings.

Line 13 of Table 1 provides first admission rates per 100,000 population for Massachusetts by quinquennial periods and for 1885. The last period in our series, 1880–84, coincides with the first years of Elkind's series. His data provide a mean rate of 54.3 per 100,000 general population for 1881–84, whereas our rate is 57.8. Since Elkind did not include patients in town almshouses, the two rates are, with this correction, in excellent agreement. In Line 14 of the same table we give the 1940 Massachusetts first admission rate standardized for age on the Massachusetts population during different periods of our 19th century series. It is apparent that even after standardization a very large difference between the contemporary and the 19th century first admission rates still remains. We have, however, drawn the reader's attention to these total rates largely in order to emphasize their complete inadequacy for the purpose of making comparisons with the contemporary period, and thus to dismiss them from further consideration. We shall show that, independent of the age structure of the population, the age pattern of first admissions was radically different in the 19th century from what it is today.[39] Consequently we shall find that the degree of difference between earlier and con-

39. By an age pattern of admissions independent of the age structure of a population we refer, of course, to the fact that two populations having the same age structure and identical total admission rates may still have very different age-specific rates.

temporary rates is very markedly a function of the particular age groups whose rates one compares. Specifically we shall show that given appropriate contemporary comparisons, the 19th century rates for the central age groups 20-50 achieved parity with those of today two to three generations ago. Only age-specific rates can reveal this high level of institutionalization during the 19th century. For these reasons we dispense with any further consideration of the essentially misleading total rates provided in Lines 13 and 14 of Table 1.

Before examining the actual age-specific first admission rates for 1840–85, the reader's attention is directed to Table 2 and Chart I. These present the distribution of age-specific rates for Massachusetts, 1870–85, and Massachusetts, 1939–41, for a *standard* total rate—that is, they show the *relative* magnitudes of age-specific rates for an *equal* number of admissions per 100,000 population during the two periods.[40] From Chart I it is clearly apparent that even though a *total* contemporary rate very considerably exceeds one for the 19th century period, it

TABLE 2

DISTRIBUTION OF AGE-SPECIFIC RATES FOR AN EQUAL
NUMBER OF FIRST ADMISSIONS PER 100,000 GENERAL
POPULATION, MASSACHUSETTS, 1870–85 AND 1939–41

(Note: These are not to be interpreted as observed or actual rates.)

AGE	1870–85	1939–41 *	RATIO
10-19	31.2	46.9	.67
20-29	133.0	100.0	1.33
30-39	183.0	124.5	1.47
40-49	178.0	125.5	1.42
50-59	144.5	136.0	1.06
60-	128.0	232.0	.55
TOTAL	100.0	100.0	1.00

* Source: Computed from data in U. S. Department of Commerce, *Patients in Mental Institutions,* 1939 1940, 1941, and Commonwealth of Massachusetts, *Annual Report of the Commissioner of Mental Health,* 1939.

40. Although the 19th century period is represented by data from 1870–85, essentially the same distribution exists for the earlier years, 1840–69, as well.

does not necessarily follow that the 19th century rates are exceeded in the central age groups. The most striking characteristic of the two curves is, of course, the heavy concentration of 19th century admissions in the central age groups, with a subsequent decline in rates for the older age groups, as compared with the progressive increase in rates with age in the contem-

CHART I

AFTER TABLE 2

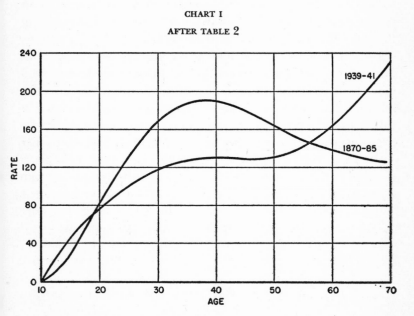

porary period. It is this point which makes so completely futile the attempt to prove, on the basis of *total* first admission rates, that the incidence of mental disease was as great years ago as it is now. Later we shall discuss more fully the significance of the age-specific rate distributions during these two periods; here we may simply note that today in Massachusetts approximately 90 percent of all first admissions 70 years of age and over and 75 percent of first admissions 60 years of age and over are accounted for by psychoses of the senium. Since our analysis will for the time being concentrate more especially on the age groups, 20-50, this means that our 19th and 20th century comparisons are in effect comparisons of rates for the psychoses incident to these ages.

We turn now to Tables 3 and 4 which provide age-specific first admission rates for 1840–85, Table 4 providing these rates by sex for the last quinquennial period and for 1885.[41] Age distributions of first admissions by sex became available only in 1880. We have, however, almost complete data on the sex distribution of total admissions (first and readmissions) throughout our period. This has enabled us to compute the ratios of male to female rates, which by decades beginning with 1840 are 1.03, 1.14, 1.11, and 1.18. For the last 5 years, 1880–85, the ratio was 1.12. We were also able to secure, through the period, data covering a considerable proportion of our admissions by age and by sex. These data reveal that the sex ratios cited above for total rates hold very uniformly throughout the individual age-specific rates.[42] Consequently the data of Table 3 can be rendered sex-specific by using the sex ratios given above. We emphasize this here because we shall later make use of this in some of our comparisons. The ratio of male to female rates has risen considerably in the contemporary period. In 1939 in Massachusetts it was 1.34.[43] Consequently the sex-specificity as well as the age-specificity of comparisons becomes of some importance.

41. In these and in all subsequent tables, admissions for ages under 20 have been allocated to the age group 10-19. Admissions under 10 years of age are so rare that scarcely any error results from this procedure. All age-specific rates are calculated on a basis of 100,000 population of the corresponding ages.

42. Thus, if the total sex ratio for 1850–59 is applied to each age group individually, we arrive at a sex and age distribution of admissions that differs so little from the observed sex and age distribution of admissions to Northampton, Taunton, and Worcester (1855–59) that a X^2 test of homogeneity for the two sets of distributions gives $P = .93$.

43. Calculated from data in: Commonwealth of Massachusetts, *Annual Report of the Commissioners of Mental Health for the Year Ending November 30, 1939,* Public Document No. 117 (1940).

TABLE 3

AGE-SPECIFIC FIRST-ADMISSION RATES, MASSACHUSETTS,
BY 5-YEAR PERIODS, 1840–84 AND 1885

AGE	1840-1844	1845-1849	1850-1854	1855-1859	1860-1864	1865-1869	1870-1874	1875-1879	1880-1884	1885
10-19	12.2	13.4	14.4	16.4	15.4	14.5	15.8	19.1	17.2	18.6
20-29	50.1	51.8	52.5	62.6	59.0	62.7	70.0	74.0	76.5	84.6
30-39	71.7	73.8	69.8	82.0	78.0	75.3	101.0	104.1	99.5	109.2
40-49	80.5	80.6	83.6	92.3	85.0	71.5	97.0	99.4	99.7	109.0
50-59	77.5	85.5	61.7	63.5	62.9	72.7	77.4	78.9	83.4	90.0
60-	50.1	59.9	44.5	48.0	68.0	60.5	66.8	68.0	80.2	67.8
TOTAL	39.4	41.1	39.0	44.6	43.1	43.2	51.9	56.3	57.8	62.2

We remind the reader of the discussion in the text (p. 33) of the age distribution of first admissions. Here we add the following details:

We have shown in the text that the age distribution of total admissions shows almost complete identity with the age distribution of first admissions where both are known. The percentage of cases, by quinquennial periods, for which we have the exact age distribution for first and/or total admissions is

1840–44	47.6%	1865–69	73.6%
1845–49	47.8	1870–74	80.5
1850–54	63.8	1875–79	82.3
1855–59	61.8	1880–84	87.9
1860–64	79.2	1885	88.5

The cases not accounted for in the above percentages represent admissions (institutions) for which we assumed the age distribution to be the same as for those admissions whose age distribution was known. The principal danger of error in this procedure arises from the possibility that admissions to town almshouses and to the receptacles (Tewksbury, Ipswich) had an age distribution radically different from that of the regular hospital patients. That this is not the case is indicated by the following considerations: (1) The town almshouse and county receptacle patients were of much the same type; (2) descriptive accounts indicate that many first admissions simply represented persons unable, because of pressure of space, to get into the larger hospitals; and that where selectivity operated, it was with respect to the level of manageability of the patients, and not with respect to age; (3) we found some data on the age distribution of deaths of the insane at Tewksbury; we also have such data from the hospitals; these age-at-death data imply a similar age distribution of the resident population; (4) we also have an age distribution of resident patients at Ipswich (1864–65); this distribution is again similar to that of the larger hospitals and implies an age distribution of admissions similar to that of the hospitals; (5) as our coverage approaches completeness, the newly available data show a great homogeneity with the age distribution of admissions to the other hospitals.

In our analysis we shall be primarily concerned with the age group 20-50. Any error in the decennial age groups between age 20 and 50 will, in the main, be offsetting, since the primary possibility of error is in the allocation of admissions to a particular decennium rather than to the total group age 20-50. Consequently, if our rates for the age group 30-40 are too high, this would mean that our rates for the group 20-30 and/or 40-50 are too low.

TABLE 4

AGE-SPECIFIC FIRST-ADMISSION RATES BY SEX, MASSACHUSETTS,
1880–84 AND 1885

AGE	1880–1884		1885	
	MALE	FEMALE	MALE	FEMALE
10-19	19.3	14.7	22.0	15.0
20-29	87.9	66.8	96.4	75.0
30-39	103.6	95.6	111.0	107.9
40-49	104.7	95.2	110.0	108.1
50-59	88.5	78.5	102.9	78.8
60-	84.8	74.5	70.4	65.5

We wish to test the hypothesis that in the central age groups the incidence of the major mental disorders has not increased over the last two to three generations. We bring to bear on this problem first admission rates for Massachusetts in the 19th century, and the question now arises: What rates from the contemporary period should be compared with them? The most immediate comparison that suggests itself is, of course, with the contemporary Massachusetts age-specific rates. This, however, is not necessarily the most desirable choice of comparative data. Hospital admission rates are a function (a) of the actual incidence of mental disease and (b) of factors that influence the proportion and type of mentally ill persons who are hospitalized. Our comparisons should, therefore, strive to ensure as much comparability as possible with respect to these latter factors, and where strict comparability cannot be attained, we must at least take them into account in our interpretations of the 19th century and contemporary rates.

The more important extraneous factors that need to be considered in testing the hypothesis are: (a) level of hospital facilities relative to demand as measured, for example, by marked differences in the ratio of admissible patients who are rejected for lack of accommodations to the total number of admissions, or as measured by the sudden rise in admission rates resulting from the opening of new hospitals in the areas most immediately accessible to them; [44] (b) accessibility to the institutions as defined, for example, by the relation of admission rate to distance from a hospital (where other factors have been held constant); (c) motivation to use facilities for a given level of facilities available and accessible; (d) range or type of patients admitted, in terms of diagnostic class, degree of severity of the mental illness required to secure admission, and (partly related to this) whether admissions are for relatively long periods or just for a few days to permit observation or temporary care; (e) composition of the population with respect to factors (other than age) that influence admission rates both in terms of their relation to the foregoing factors and to the true incidence of mental disease, e.g., proportion of foreign-born and urban dwellers in the population. The large foreign-born, (especially Irish), immigration of the mid-19th century renders it imperative to ensure that our 19th century rates, relative to those of

44. It is not desirable, of course, to define level of facilities in terms of the number of hospital beds per population unit, since fewer beds might simply mean a lesser need rather than a lower level of facilities. Measures of "overcrowding" (patients in excess of rated capacity) are equivocal, since such overcrowding may in fact indicate that all patients seeking admission are being received despite space limitations. The rejection of admissible patients because of a lack of accommodations (under standards of space per patient not higher than those of today), and the change in admission rate immediately following upon the opening of new facilities are, on the other hand, clear evidence of unfilled hospitalization needs.

While it is not possible to provide exact comparisons of the facilities of the 19th century and the contemporary period, it should be added that in making our comparisons we have taken into account the fact that 19th century facilities are somewhat greater than may appear on the surface for the following two reasons: (a) the concentration of admissions in the central age groups meant that for these age groups a larger proportion of available space was open to them than is the case in contemporary mental hospitals where large numbers of older people are admitted; (b) the turnover of the institutional population was greater than today, thus permitting more admissions for a given number of beds. The higher rate of turnover was, however, in part due to the pressure of applications. The more manageable and incurable patients were often discharged to make room for new patients. Hospital trustees were given authority to remove such patients to relieve the pressure of new admissions. (Cf. Chapter 223, Statutes of 1862, and earlier Massachusetts Statutes.)

today, are not rendered incomparable by differing proportions of the foreign-born population and different relations of foreign-born and native-born rates. Since it is easier to discuss this matter after the presentation of the 19th century and contemporary rates, we have placed our discussion of the foreign-born at the end of this section (pp. 83-89). In the meantime the reader can be assured that the following comparisons of 19th century and contemporary rates are not affected by the foreign-born. If, however, he wishes further assurance that this is not the case, he should turn immediately to pp. 83-89.

Since the factors that influence the choice of a standard of comparison from the contemporary period were not constant through the period 1840–85, it follows that the rates chosen from the contemporary period for comparison with those of 1885 are not necessarily the appropriate ones to use in a comparison with 1860 or 1840. Consequently, in what follows we provide a variety of contemporary rates with which we compare the rates of different parts of our 19th century series; and in each case we indicate why these particular contemporary rates have been chosen for comparative purposes. The attempt to choose contemporary rates that provide the greatest constancy of the conditions (a) to (e) discussed above, must, to a considerable extent, be impressionistic. Sufficiently exact data on the factors involved, and on the weighting to be assigned to each, to permit the construction of a single quantitative measure, are not available. We have, however, in all cases chosen contemporary rates that we believe provide a severe test of the hypothesis under study—that is, we have chosen contemporary rates in which the operation of factors (a) to (e) are on the whole prejudicial to the hypothesis.

Comparison of 1885 and Contemporary
Massachusetts Rates [45]

From the standpoint of the hypothesis we are testing, the severest comparison that we can make is with contemporary Massachusetts rates. The 1940 Massachusetts first admission rate was 20 percent higher than the national average and 5 percent higher than the New England and Middle Atlantic rates.[46] This rate includes Massachusetts admissions to two Veterans' Administration hospitals and to private hospitals. It also counts as first admissions persons admitted for observation (a 10-day period) and temporary care (a 40-day period) and then discharged, these admissions comprising *one-third* of first admissions.[47] The Massachusetts population was 90 percent urban in 1940 as compared with 75 percent urban in 1880. Massachusetts has today one of the most highly developed mental hospital systems in the country, and one can scarcely suppose that the level and accessibility of facilities (relative to demand for services) was as high in 1885 as it is today. In 1939, 22.2 percent of its admissions were for nonpsychotic conditions,[48] as compared

45. In choosing the year 1885 (instead of 1880–84) we have not attempted to choose a year with maximum rates in order to make our comparisons with the present period more striking. Rates for 1885 were chosen in preference to 1880–84 because during that 5-year period the rates were rising at an increasing rate, and the 1885 rates are characteristic for the years 1883–87. Consequently, 1885 is not an isolated peak year. During the subsequent years rates continued to rise and we could, perhaps, have provided more unambiguous results by continuing our series to 1890. We were, however, content to end our series when it became apparent that we had arrived at rates for the central age groups that were equal to those of today.

46. U. S. Department of Commerce, *Patients in Mental Institutions, 1940* (Government Printing Office, Washington, 1943), pp. 8-9.

47. Commonwealth of Massachusetts, *op. cit.*, 1940, p. 153. Temporary care and observation cases do *not* include cases which, upon the termination of the observation and temporary care period, receive a regular court or voluntary commitment.

48. The percent of admissions without psychotic disorders is considerably higher for the youngest age group, much lower for the oldest age groups, and close to the mean in the central age groups.

with our estimate of 5-8 percent for the period of 1880–85 (see page 42). The evidence would seem to be overwhelming that in choosing the contemporary Massachusetts first admission rates we provide a standard of comparison in which the extraneous factors are heavily weighted against a proper test of the hypothesis under study. Our next three comparisons will provide a more adequate test of the hypothesis, but we present this initial comparison in order to indicate some of the factors involved in the choice of an appropriate standard of comparison.

Table 5 and Chart II provide the necessary data for this comparison. In view of the foregoing remarks it is somewhat astonishing to find that the 1885 female rates for the age-group 30-50 are identical with those for 1939–41. As is to be anticipated from our discussion of Chart I, this parity of rates falls off markedly in the older age groups.

TABLE 5

MALE AND FEMALE AGE-SPECIFIC FIRST-ADMISSION RATES, MASSACHUSETTS, 1885 AND 1939–41

	1885		1939–41*	
AGE	MALE	FEMALE	MALE	FEMALE
10-19	22.0	15.0	57.2	42.8
20-29	96.4	75.0	124.2	91.1
30-39	111.0	107.9	159.9	108.2
40-49	110.0	108.1	164.0	106.0
50-59	102.9	78.8	174.5	117.3
60-	70.4	65.5	279.5	223.0

* Source: U. S. Department of Commerce, *Patients in Mental Institutions*, 1939, 1940, 1941, and Commonwealth of Massachusetts, *Annual Report of the Commissioner of Mental Health*, 1939.

The contemporary male Massachusetts rates show, in this comparison, a substantial growth over those of our last quinquennial period, amounting to an increase of approximately 30 percent for the age group 20-30, and 50 percent for the age

CHART II

AFTER TABLE 5

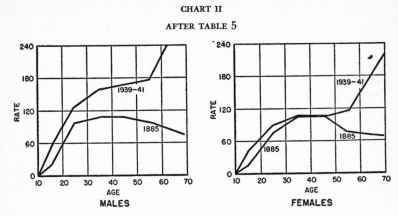

MALES   FEMALES

group 30-50. Why do not the 1885 male rates show the same comparability with contemporary rates as do the female rates? The difference is very largely accounted for by (a) the larger proportion of temporary care and observation cases among the males (39.5 percent for men and 27.8 percent for women); and (b) the larger proportion of nonpsychotic admissions among men than among women (25.5 percent for men, and 17.9 percent for women).[49] In part, these considerations overlap, since temporary care and observation cases have a larger proportion of admissions without psychosis than do the more permanent types of admissions.

The majority of the observation and temporary care cases remained in hospitals only 10 days before discharge and thus represent a type of psychiatric service and legal and social service procedure scarcely represented in our earlier period.[50] Fur-

49. Commonwealth of Massachusetts, *op. cit.*, 1940, pp. 148, 323.

50. We have exact data on this point for years somewhat earlier than 1885. Thus, of the 1074 first admissions to Northampton Hospital for the years 1858–70, only 2.5 percent were discharged within a month of their admission; most of these were the few cases of delirium tremens that the hospital received. At Worcester Hospital only 7.3 percent of patients admitted during the years 1854–61 were discharged within a month or less. Descriptive material indicates that this picture remains essentially unchanged in the latter part of our period.

ther, as we have seen, the admissions without psychosis form a
very much higher proportion of admissions than in the late
19th century period. For both of these reasons our initial comparison constitutes, more particularly in the case of males, an
inappropriate choice of comparative data. We now turn to a
comparison in which comparability of conditions is more fully
attained.

*Comparison of 1885 Rates with Contemporary
Massachusetts Rates for Admissions with
Mental Disorder*

By using this comparison we are able to correct only par-
tially the overrepresentation, in the contemporary rates, of a
class of admission largely excluded in the older rates. The category of admissions "with mental disorders" still includes a very
substantial number of temporary care and observation cases,
these still comprising 24 percent of first admissions "with mental disorder"; further, this category also includes persons admitted with a diagnosis of neurosis or psychoneurosis, these
constituting approximately 3 percent of admissions with mental disorder. Given this situation and the fact that the other extraneous factors discussed earlier, which are prejudicial to the
hypothesis, are still operative, it is quite clear that the comparison we are now about to make still affords a severe test of
our hypothesis.

Table 6 and Chart III provide the necessary data for our
present comparison. They reveal that the 1885 female rates
exceed the contemporary rates for the entire age range 20-50.
The 1885 male rates show substantial agreement with the contemporary rates for ages up to 40; the contemporary rate for the

TABLE 6

MALE AND FEMALE AGE-SPECIFIC FIRST-ADMISSION RATES,
MASSACHUSETTS, 1885, AND AGE-SPECIFIC FIRST-ADMISSION
(WITH MENTAL DISORDER) RATES, MASSACHUSETTS, 1917–40.

| | 1885 | | 1917–40* | |
AGE	MALE	FEMALE	MALE	FEMALE
10-19	22.0	15.0	25	22
20-29	96.4	75.0	99	72
30-39	111.0	107.9	115	90
40-49	110.0	108.1	124	102
50-59	102.9	78.8	132	109
60-	70.4	65.5	244	198

* Source: U. S. Public Health Service, *Mental Health in Later Maturity*, Suppl.
No. 168, p. 114.

age group 40-50 is 13 percent in excess of the corresponding
rate for 1885.[51]

We thus conclude from this comparison that between 1885
and the contemporary period there has been no increase in the
frequency of admissions among men and women in the central
age groups.

CHART III

AFTER TABLE 6

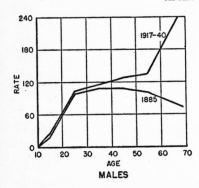

MALES

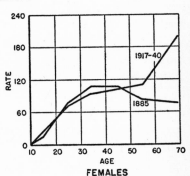

FEMALES

51. The slight difference between the male 1885 and 1940 rates for the age
group 20-40 is not significant; $P = .33$. For the age group 40-50, $P = .08$. The
values of P here and in later tests are for a "one tailed" test of significance.
This is appropriate in testing our hypothesis against the alternative hypothesis
that contemporary rates exceed those of the 19th century.

Comparison of 1885 Massachusetts Rates with Contemporary Massachusetts Rates for Court and Voluntary Admissions

In this comparison we exclude the observation and temporary care first admissions, but include all regular admissions to public and private hospitals both with and without mental disorder. Since the age distribution of court and voluntary commitments was not available for 1940, we present data for 1930. This comparison (Table 7 and Chart IV) reveals that the male 1885 rate for the combined age group 20-40 slightly exceeds that of the contemporary period and that the 1885 female rates for ages 20-50 exceed the corresponding 1930 figures. Reference to Table 3 and the sex ratio data given on p. 48 also shows that the female rates for the combined group 20-50 years of age had achieved parity with the contemporary rate 15 years earlier, that is by 1870.

With respect to type of admissions represented in the rates of the two periods compared, the above comparison is probably the most equitable of the three we have so far discussed.

TABLE 7

MALE AND FEMALE AGE-SPECIFIC FIRST-ADMISSION RATES, MASSACHUSETTS, 1885, AND AGE-SPECIFIC FIRST-ADMISSION (COURT AND VOLUNTARY) RATES, MASSACHUSETTS, 1930

	1885		1930*	
AGE	MALE	FEMALE	MALE	FEMALE
10-19	22.0	15.0	25.6	23.8
20-29	96.4	75.0	90.6	70.0
30-39	111.0	107.9	111.7	86.9
40-49	110.0	108.1	124.7	100.0
50-59	102.9	78.8	128.5	120.0
60-	70.4	65.5	254.0	206.5

* Source: Commonwealth of Massachusetts, *Annual Report of the Commissioner of Mental Diseases for the Year Ending November 30, 1930,* Public Document No. 117 (1931).

It leads, however, to the conclusion arrived at from the preceding comparison, namely, that no increase in admission rates for the central age groups has occurred during the last 60 to 70 years.

CHART IV

AFTER TABLE 7

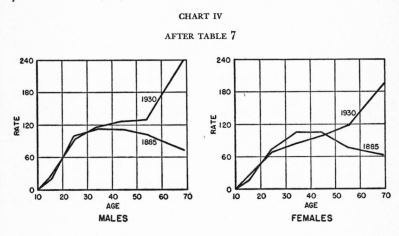

MALES

FEMALES

Comparison of 1885 Massachusetts Rates with Contemporary Rates for Northeastern United States

The comparison of Massachusetts late 19th century rates with those for contemporary Massachusetts imposes a quite severe test of our hypothesis. Nonetheless, for the central age groups, the hypothesis has stood up to the test applied. A further comparison that suggests itself is to juxtapose our late 19th century rates for Massachusetts with first admission rates for the combined Northeastern states (New England and Middle Atlantic states). The two preceding comparisons have provided somewhat greater comparability with respect to the classes of patients received in the two periods. In terms of comparability of level of facilities available, a better comparison can probably be achieved by using rates for a larger area in which the facilities may be presumed to deviate less from those of our late 19th century period. It would be desirable to provide a comparison which simultaneously attempts to equate level of facilities and class of patients, but the contemporary data do not permit this very readily. Our inability to make such a comparison means, of course, an increase in the severity of the test to which our hypothesis is subjected. In choosing the Northeastern states for our next comparison, we have by no means selected a low-rate area. These states have a first admission rate that is 20 percent above the average for the country as a whole. They are, taken together, highly urbanized and industrialized states and the great proportion of their population and admissions come from states that have well-developed mental hospital systems.[52] Further, in making this comparison we include all admissions, both with and without mental disorder, to state, county, and city mental hospitals, Veterans Administration hospitals, and private mental hospitals. Table 8 and Chart V show the relation of Massachusetts 1885 and Northeastern 1940 age-specific first admission rates. Here again we

TABLE 8

MALE AND FEMALE AGE-SPECIFIC FIRST-ADMISSION RATES, MASSACHUSETTS, 1885, AND NORTHEASTERN STATES, 1940

	1885		1940*	
AGE	MALE	FEMALE	MALE	FEMALE
10-19	22.0	15.0	35.1	25.3
20-29	96.4	75.0	95.1	78.9
30-39	111.0	107.9	115.0	105.0
40-49	110.0	108.1	132.0	110.7
50-59	102.9	78.8	140.3	120.5
60-	70.4	65.5	267.5	232.0

* Source: U. S. Department of Commerce, *Patients in Mental Institutions*, 1939, 1940, 1941.

52. The Northeastern states were 76.5 percent urban in 1940 as compared with 74.7 percent for Massachusetts in 1880. Six of the nine Northeastern states had, in 1940, first admission rates over 100. There were only eleven such states in the United States in that year. (U. S. Department of Commerce, *Patients in Mental Institutions*, 1940 (Washington, 1943), pp. 8-9.)

find that the female rates for 1885 show complete parity with those of 1940 for the age groups 20-50. The male rates for 1885 show complete parity for the age groups 20-40; in the age

CHART V

AFTER TABLE 8

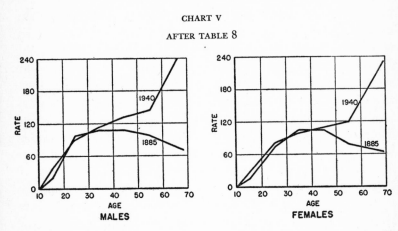

MALES   FEMALES

group 40-50 the contemporary rate exceeds the 1885 rate by 17 percent.[53] These results are, then, almost identical with those provided by the preceding comparison.

Massachusetts Rates from 1860 to 1885

In our next comparison we shall move back to approximately the midpoint of our 19th century series (1855–59). Before doing so a few remarks on Massachusetts rates for the intervening years, 1860–85, are in order. The rates in the central age groups for 1860–69 show a small decline over those of 1855–59. This is apparently not the result of random fluctuation but represents, at least for the earlier years of the decennium, the effect of the Civil War. The decline in rates was

53. For the female 1885 and 1940 rates, ages 20-50, $P = .43$. For the males, ages 20-29, the 1885 rate is slightly higher than the 1940 rate; for the age group 30-39, $P = .33$; and for the age group 40-49, $P = .015$.

noted by Dr. Jarvis and attributed to the Civil War.[54] Our own analysis shows that the effect of the war was somewhat more complicated than he was aware. In 1860–64 the decline in rates is entirely accounted for by Massachusetts, exclusive of Suffolk County (largely the Boston area); in Suffolk County the rates rose during these years. In the following 5 years the situation was reversed. Suffolk County showed a marked decline, but the rest of Massachusetts showed the postwar increase that one normally anticipates. The decline in the Boston rate was almost entirely due to a very considerable and sudden postwar increase in the population without a corresponding increase in admissions. The Massachusetts rates, exclusive of Suffolk County, behaved in very much the same fashion as rates did during and after World Wars I and II.

Beginning with 1870–74 the rates showed a steady but not very large increase up to 1885. A considerable share of this increase was due to the opening of Danvers Hospital, which rapidly became one of the largest hospitals in the state, and to the opening of the new Worcester Hospital. Given these very considerable accretions in facilities and the fact that, in any case, for the age groups 30-40 and 40-50 the differences between the 1870–74 and 1885 rates are not significant at the 5-percent probability level, we can treat the period of 1870–85 as being, on the whole, homogeneous from the standpoint of the incidence of mental disease in the central age groups.

Comparison of Massachusetts 1855–59 Rates with United States 1940 Rates for First Admissions with Psychosis

In going back to a period almost a century ago one is hard pressed to know what comparative data from the contemporary

---

54. Edward Jarvis, *The Political Economy of Health* (Boston, 1874), p. 389.

period can be selected as providing some measure of equivalence with the limited facilities for hospitalization available in the mid-19th century. Some indication of the unsatisfied pressure for hospitalization existing at this time is afforded by the effect on admission rates of Bristol and Hampshire County residents when Taunton and Northampton Hospitals located in these counties opened in 1854 and 1858. In the 8 years preceding the opening of Taunton, Bristol County residents had an admission rate to the major Massachusetts hospitals of 25 per 100,000 population. In the 8 years following the opening of Taunton, the annual admission rate rose over 100 percent to 56 per 100,000 population. A similar, but even greater effect, was occasioned by the opening of Northampton Hospital in Hampshire County. At this period the "law of distance," whereby the frequency of admissions tends to be inverse to the distance from a hospital, was very strongly operative. Counties that had a mental hospital immediately accessible to them had admission rates that were double those of other counties.[55] The "law of distance" still operates today, but with much diminished force. We have computed for contemporary Massachusetts the average total admission rate for the six counties with mental hospitals (exclusive of Suffolk County) and the seven counties without a hospital. These have rates of 133.1 and 117.8 respectively.[56] Their ratio of 1.13 contrasts sharply with a ratio of approximately 2.0 for the mid-19th century. When Taunton Hospital opened, counties less favored with respect to proximity to it showed relatively little increase in admissions. Since there is no reason to believe that Bristol and Hampshire Counties had an undue number of insane, one can readily imagine

55. For data on the "law of distance," see the rather remarkable study by Edward Jarvis, "Influence of Distance From and Nearness To an Insane Hospital on Its Use by the People," *American Journal of Insanity*, XXII (1866), pp. 361-407.
56. Computed from data in Commonwealth of Massachusetts, *op. cit.*, 1940, p. 236.

the effect on mid-19th century admission rates of increases in other counties similar to those which took place in Bristol and Hampshire Counties. Even today the opening of new hospitals still leads to small increments in hospitalization rates. But this increase is of a completely different order as compared with the increases that followed the opening of new hospitals in the 19th century period. This effect on admission rates resulting from the opening of new facilities is one of the two quantitative indices of relative levels of unfulfilled hospitalization needs discussed on pp. 50-51.

In view of the foregoing considerations and taking into account also that in this earlier period admissions become increasingly restricted to the more severe cases of mental derangement, we have selected as a standard of comparison with the contemporary period first admission rates for psychoses to all mental hospitals, public and private, for the United States. Massachusetts was 50.7 percent urban in 1850 and 59.6 percent urban in 1860. This compares with 56.5 percent for the United States as a whole in 1940. As we shall show later (pp. 83-89), differences in the proportion of foreign-born do not affect our comparisons. In effect, then, we are saying that the various conditions inhibiting admissions to mental hospitals were at least no less in Massachusetts of 1855–59 than they are currently in the United States as a whole. Probably there is no state in the Union today in which the restrictions on admission to institutions for the mentally ill approach those that existed in Massachusetts in 1855–59.[57] We feel that we are providing a comparison that is probably prejudicial to a confirmation of the hypothesis we are testing, and that those familiar with the his-

57. In 1840, for every ten Massachusetts residents received at Worcester Hospital, there were four who were turned away for lack of accommodation (see pp. 66-67 below). We do not have comparable quantitative data for the period 1855–59, but the official reports make it clear that the rejection rate was still considerable at this time.

tory of institutional developments in this period would agree with this supposition.

Table 9 and Chart VI provide comparisons, then, between Massachusetts first admission rates for 1855–59 and rates for

TABLE 9

MALE AND FEMALE AGE-SPECIFIC FIRST-ADMISSION RATES, MASSACHUSETTS, 1855–59, AND UNITED STATES AGE-SPECIFIC FIRST-ADMISSION (WITH PSYCHOSIS) RATES, 1940

	1855–59		1940*	
AGE	MALE	FEMALE	MALE	FEMALE
10-19	17.5	15.4	19.1	14.1
20-29	66.9	58.6	71.5	59.1
30-39	87.5	76.7	92.5	81.7
40-49	98.5	86.5	115.7	91.7
50-59	67.8	59.5	121.6	103.6
60-	51.3	45.0	215.0	165.5

* Source: U. S. Department of Commerce, "Estimates for Psychotic First Admissions to Mental Hospitals, by Age and Sex: 1940 to 1945," *Current Population Reports*, Series P-85, No. 18.

psychotic first admissions to public and private mental hospitals in the United States for 1940. This comparison shows that the 1940 male rates exceed those of 1855–59 by 6-9 percent in the age groups under 40, and 17 percent in the age groups

CHART VI

AFTER TABLE 9

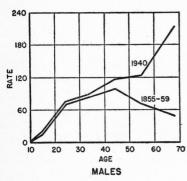

MALES

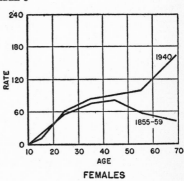

FEMALES

40-50. The 1940 female rates for ages under 30 are the same as for the period 1855–59 and for the ages 30-50 exceed the older rates by only 6 percent.[58] Although the lack of age-specific rates for the various states of the United States today prevents precise comparison without considerable computational work, we would judge that the 1855–59 Massachusetts rate for ages 30-50 equal or exceed the corresponding rates of 10 to 15 states in the United States today. Assuming the general adequacy of the standard of comparison used in Table 9, and given the essential parity of the female rates and the only slightly greater difference in the male rates for ages under 40, we must conclude that there is no evidence here of any increase in the central age groups in the incidence of mental disease between 1855 and 1940.

Comparison of Massachusetts 1840–44 Rates with the Contemporary Period

We were hard pressed to choose a standard of comparison for our 1855–59 rates. When we turn back to our first quinquennial period, we are quite at a loss to know what area or areas today can be selected to provide a legitimate comparison with this early period. In assessing the 1840–44 rates it should be recalled that the first mental hospital in Massachusetts (McLean Hospital), confined largely to the well-to-do, was opened only in 1818. The Worcester Hospital had only been in operation 8 years when our period opened and the South Boston Hospital, only 1 year. Some conception of the limited facilities available at this time is perhaps conveyed by the fact that during the first 6 years of its operation as the first state mental hos-

58. The difference between the 1855–59 and 1940 male rates in the central age groups is significant at the 5-percent level only for the age groups 20-30 and 40-50. None of the differences for the female rates is significant at this probability level.

pital, Worcester received additions of four wings which were
no sooner completed than they were immediately "filled to the
overflowing." As we pointed out earlier, Worcester accounts
for 50 per cent of the first admissions during our initial decade
and these admissions were restricted by law to "the furious and
dangerous." Both in 1839 and 1840 the ratio of applications
rejected for lack of room to those accepted was .6 for all rejections, and .4 for rejections of Massachusetts residents alone.[59]
In this period it was by no means uncommon for even the most
severely deranged persons to be kept at home chained and confined under the most appalling conditions. We do not present,
for this earliest period, comparative tables similar to those in
the preceding sections. We simply note here that the Massachusetts rates for the central age groups for 1840–44 are as high
as contemporary rates for the three states in the United States
with the lowest rates in 1940, namely Maine, North Dakota,
and Florida. The Massachusetts rate for 1840–44 for the age
group 30-60 exceed by 5 percent those of Maine for 1940. However, the 1941 Maine rates exceed the Massachusetts 1840–44
rate by 35 percent in the age groups 30 and under.[60] We note
also that the female first admission psychosis rates for 1940 for

59. Computed from data in *Seventh Annual Report . . . Worcester* (Boston,
1840), p. 67, and *Eighth Annual Report . . . Worcester* (Boston, 1841), p. 5.
The proportion of persons explicitly rejected for lack of room does not, of
course, take into account additional cases who, because of the admission situation, would not even attempt to gain admission. If we assume that the rejection rate was similar at the other hospitals during this period, it follows that
more adequate facilities would have led, at a minimum, to a 40-percent increase
in the admission rate of 1840–44. This would bring the 1840–44 rate up to
the level of the later 1875 rate, and would further mean that the 1840–44
rate for the age group 30-50 equals or exceeds the corresponding rate of about
15 to 20 states today.

60. Maine in 1940 was 40.5 percent urban and Massachusetts in 1840 was
37.9 percent urban. An urban-rural distribution of patients for one of the
two Maine mental hospitals indicates that in this state the rural and urban
rates are probably the same. It would seem, therefore, that the Massachusetts
1840–44 rates are, for the age group 30-60, higher than contemporary urban
Maine rates.

the United States as a whole exceed the 1840–44 female rates in the age groups 30-50 *by only 13 percent.* Given the restrictions on admissions in this earliest period it is quite impossible to suppose that this difference reflects a real increase in the incidence of mental disorders among women in these age groups in the intervening 100 years.

Comparison of Suffolk County, Massachusetts, 19th Century Rates with Contemporary Rates for New York City

So far we have dealt in our analysis with Massachusetts as a single unit. There are, however, several reasons why a special analysis of the Boston area recommends itself. In the first place, some interest is attached to the question whether in the 19th century the disparity usually found today between rates for large metropolitan centers and for smaller towns and country areas existed in the earlier period.[61] Secondly, and this is more important for our present purposes, we may presume that comparisons of 19th century and contemporary metropolitan rates provide a somewhat greater constancy of conditions than is feasible when state rates as a whole are compared. Large urban

---

61. We say "large metropolitan centers" rather than "cities" or "urban areas" designedly. Much of the presumed difference between urban and rural rates is often accounted for by the largest city in a state. Thus, in Massachusetts, Boston had in 1939 a first admission rate of 167. Rates for cities between 20-50,000, 50-100,000, and 100-250,000 ranged from 100 to 105. These rates are no higher than the rural rate which was 102. To be sure rural areas in Massachusetts are, due to the population density, less "rural" than in larger states. In 1939 rural rates were 11 percent higher than rates for towns between 2,500-25,000 population. (Commonwealth of Massachusetts, *op. cit.*, 1940, p. 165.)

In the 19th century period urban-rural differences in rates were more marked. Thus our calculations show that in 1885 the rate for areas with a population of over 10,000 (but excluding Suffolk County) was 30 percent higher than the admission rate for areas under 10,000 population. In 1939 this excess was only about 5 percent. This is consistent with the observed convergence over time of urban and rural rates in Illinois. (Cf. American Psychopathological Association, *op. cit.*, p. 74.)

centers probably have social characteristics that are more continuous over time.[62] Perhaps more important is the fact that
Boston residents, throughout our entire period, had two hospitals locally available (McLean and South Boston), and while
one was confined largely to the rich both in and outside of Boston, and the other had rather limited accommodations, so that
most Boston patients were sent to state hospitals outside of Suffolk County, nevertheless they did counteract to some extent
the operation of the "law of distance."

   The possibility of comparing Suffolk County rates with contemporary metropolitan rates rests, of course, on the capacity
to segregate admissions to Massachusetts institutions by county
of residence. The South Boston Hospital occasions no difficulty, since it was a Suffolk County hospital for county patients
and its admissions can all be allocated to that county. McLean
Hospital reports provide data on the county of residence of its
patients during the last part of our period; for 1866 we have
residence data from Dr. Jarvis. On the basis of the more adequate later data we have allocated .3 of McLean admissions to
Suffolk County, although our 1866 data indicate .4 as a closer
estimate for the earlier part of the period. We thus use what is
probably an overly conservative estimate, especially during the

62. This is indicated in one particular respect by the data of the present
study. Whereas in the rest of Massachusetts the peak rate is for the age group
30-39, the Suffolk County data consistently show the highest rate in the age
group 40-49 or older. Thus the 19th century metropolitan rates conform more
closely to the contemporary distribution of age-specific rates. The reason for
this is indicated in a later discussion (p. 82). It should be added here, that
although the rates for the oldest age groups may be subject to some bias, this
is not the case for the age group 40-49; consequently our later discussion of
possible biases in the rates for the oldest age groups does not affect the above
observation. The propriety of speaking of Suffolk County or Boston as an urban
or metropolitan center is indicated by the following population data for Suffolk County and Boston. Population of Suffolk County, in thousands: 1840, 96;
1850, 145; 1860, 193; 1870, 271; 1880, 388. Population of Boston, in thousands:
1840, 93; 1850, 137; 1860, 179; 1870, 251; 1880, 363. Most of the Suffolk County
population not accounted for by Boston is provided by the city of Chelsea.
Suffolk County was 97.5 percent urban in 1840 and 99.3 percent urban in 1880.

earlier years of the series, but we did not want to run the risk of inflating our urban rates. For Worcester Hospital, and the other state hospitals as they came into existence, the annual reports provide exact residence data.[63] Over 90 percent of our 1860–80 Suffolk County admissions, 72 percent of 1850–59 admissions, and 56 percent of 1840–49 admissions are based on exact county of residence data, the residue being accounted for by our conservative McLean estimates. We have good evidence that the first-to-total-admission ratio is the same for Suffolk County as for the rest of the state; and whenever only total admission data were available, we used this ratio in estimating first admissions.[64] We have assumed that the age distribution of admissions is the same for Suffolk County as for the state as a whole. We have assumed this on the basis of the age distribution of South Boston Hospital patients who are all Suffolk County residents. This distribution is not significantly different from that for the state as a whole (see note 17, p. 32). The population of Suffolk County is more heavily weighted with persons in the age group 20-50 than is the rest of the state. Consequently, if the use of the age distribution of state admissions for Suffolk County admissions introduces any biases at all in our Suffolk County rates, they will be offsetting and of the following types: an inflation of the rates for ages 10-20 and for 50 and over, a downward bias for ages 20-40, while the age group 40-50 is roughly unbiased. As we are principally interested in the central age groups 20-50, our rates for these ages may, both for this

63. Bookkeeping in connection with the system of financial accountability for patients made accurate place-of-residence records very important in the 19th century period.

64. For South Boston Hospital we used, of course, the first-to-total-admission ratio for that hospital. In years for which first admission data were not directly available for McLean and the state hospitals, Suffolk County admissions were taken to have the same ratio of first-to-total admissions as the total patient body received at each hospital. That this is a conservative procedure with respect to our hypothesis is clearly indicated by the fact that state hospitals made up mostly of Suffolk County residents had, in fact, a somewhat higher ratio of first-to-total admissions than did other state hospitals.

reason and those given earlier, be taken as quite conservative estimates. We emphasize this because the rates that we are about to present may astonish the reader and we wish to assure him that he is not dealing with inflated rates in the central age groups.

The only large urban center for which we were able to find contemporary first admission age-specific rates, including admissions to both state and private institutions, is New York City. Malzberg [65] has provided such data for New York City for 1929–31. At the time his study was made data were not available on voluntary admissions to licensed institutions. We have corrected Malzberg's data upward by 14-27 percent in the various age groups, so that the New York City rates that we provide in comparison with Suffolk County represent a very complete first admission rate.[66]

Table 10 presents Suffolk County rates for 1840–1880. The data for our comparison with New York City are, however, presented in Table 11 and Chart VII. They reveal that in

TABLE 10

AGE-SPECIFIC FIRST-ADMISSION RATES, SUFFOLK COUNTY RESIDENTS, 1840–79

AGE	1840–1844	1845–1849	1850–1854	1855–1859	1860–1864	1865–1869	1870–1874	1875–1879
10-19	23.7	25.8	29.1	31.9	33.7	24.3	26.6	32.5
20-29	76.1	78.0	83.5	94.7	103.5	88.4	96.5	111.5
30-39	107.0	111.4	108.0	126.0	137.6	108.5	136.8	160.0
40-49	147.0	146.0	156.2	177.3	185.5	112.8	150.0	168.2
50-59	193.0	215.0	162.0	141.0	161.0	128.0	144.3	162.0
60-	167.5	202.5	154.0	148.3	241.0	161.0	149.5	174.0
TOTAL	70.0	73.3	72.3	79.1	88.5	69.8	81.8	94.3

65. Benjamin Malzberg, "The Expectation of Mental Disease in New York City, 1930," *Mental Hygiene*, XXI (1937), pp. 289-90.

66. Although exact age-specific rates are not available for New York City for any year after 1931, computations indicate that for ages under 50 the 1930 rates are substantially the same as for 1940 and later. New York City is here taken to comprise the boroughs of Bronx, Brooklyn, Manhattan, and Queens.

TABLE 11

*AGE-SPECIFIC FIRST-ADMISSION RATES, SUFFOLK COUNTY,
MASSACHUSETTS, 1840–44, 1855–59, 1875–79,
AND NEW YORK CITY, 1929–31*

	SUFFOLK COUNTY		NEW YORK CITY	
Age	1840–44	1855–59	1875–79	1929–31
10-19	23.7	31.9	32.5	34.4
20-29	76.1	94.7	111.5	100.3
30-39	107.0	126.0	160.0	119.5
40-49	147.0	177.3	168.2	136.0
50-59	193.0	141.0	162.0	150.5
60-	167.5	148.3	174.0	340.0

1840–44 Suffolk County had higher rates than contemporary
New York City in the age group 40-60 and, by the mid-19th
century period, almost uniformly higher rates except in the
oldest age group. The reader may at this point feel that we
have proved too much. We must confess that when these re-

CHART VII

AFTER TABLE 11

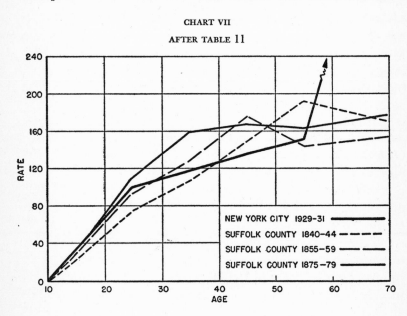

sults became evident we ourselves felt intimidated by them. However a thorough reexamination of our data and our procedures has convinced us that these findings must stand.

It may be supposed that our Suffolk County rates are inflated by the foreign-born, especially Irish, population of the county. In this connection we refer the reader to our later discussion in which this is shown not to be the case (pp. 83-89). Here we simply point out the following: (a) The foreign-born population of Suffolk County was only about 10 percent in 1840; the great influx of Irish immigrants had not begun in our earliest period, 1840–44, and yet the Suffolk County rates for this period are already higher than for New York City in two of the age groups. (b) The foreign-born constituted 33.5 percent of the Suffolk County population in 1875, but in New York City in 1930, 34 percent of the population was also foreign-born; and these foreign-born also had higher age-specific rates than native whites (the ratio for ages 20-60 is 1.2). (c) In addition, 4.7 percent of the 1930 New York City population was Negro, this group having markedly higher rates than the white population; whereas in Suffolk County the Negro population was negligible. (d) As we show in our later discussion the 19th century ratio of foreign-born to native-born rates was higher than today, but this represents, *relative to any comparison with the contemporary period,* a lowered capacity for native-born to be hospitalized in competition with the foreign-born. As compared with the contemporary period the foreign-born-to-native-born ratio indicates a lower rate of hospitalization for the *native-born* relative to the incidence of mental disease among them, and not an inflation of foreign-born rates relative to their rates today. (e) In addition it is necessary to recall the overwhelmingly superior facilities and motivation to hospitalization present in a city such as New York today as compared with 19th century Suffolk County. For these reasons we do not believe that it is at all possible to "explain away" the higher Suffolk County rates by reference to the foreign-born. Our hypothesis only requires a parity of rates between Suffolk County and New York City. Even subtracting the excess of Suffolk County, which is more than ample to take care of any possible "correction" that anyone might want to apply to the older rates, the hypothesis still stands confirmed.

Actually, of course, the findings that we present suggest that the incidence of the psychoses was *higher* in Suffolk County during the 19th century than in New York today. It should be emphasized that the higher Suffolk County rates occur without any adjustment being made for differences in facilities or class of patients received. When one more especially considers the very limited facilities available in the early part of our period, the restriction of admissions to the "violent and furious" at Worcester, and the fact that McLean was largely for the very well-to-do, the comparison becomes still more astonishing. We are not prepared to argue from our findings that the incidence of the psychoses was greater in Suffolk County in the mid-19th century than in New York today, but is is proper to point out that the data lend considerable plausability to this interpretation, and more especially so in the case of the female rates. We have not presented sex-specific rates for Suffolk County, but our data clearly indicate that the Suffolk County female rates exceed those of New York City to a greater extent than does the total rate.

*Comparison of Oneida County, New York,
1843–65, with New York State Rates, 1930*

In dealing with the 19th century period one might possibly suppose that such rates as we have shown were unique to Massachusetts. Although other states do not so readily permit computations for this period of the sort made for Massachusetts, the following analysis of Oneida County, New York, may be of some supporting value. We have, thanks to the indefatigable labors of Dr. Jarvis, the admissions, 1843–65, of Oneida County residents to the New York State Hospital in Utica, Oneida County, which opened in 1843.[67] These admissions give a total admission rate (first and readmissions) of 36.1 per 100,000 population. Let us assume that the opportunity for hospitalization and incentives for hospitalization at this early period in Oneida County were not greater than those that exist today for the state of New York as a whole. We may then ask how the Oneida County rate compares with a contemporary New York rate. The New York rate for 1930 for first and readmissions was approximately 97.[68] This is 2.7 times greater than the Oneida County rate in the mid-19th century. But the 1930 New York State rate is a function of, among other things, the age composition and urban-rural distribution of the New York State population in 1930, and of the distribution of age-specific rates.

If we adjust the 1930 New York State rate for the relevant demographic conditions in Oneida County of 1850, we find that the ratio of the 1930 rate to the rate for 1843–65 drops successively from 2.7 to 2.0, to 1.5, and finally to 1.2. These data are shown more fully in Table 12. We do not feel that this particular line of reasoning is the most useful one for demonstrating the parity of rates a century ago and today. However it does illustrate rather forcibly the danger involved in assuming that markedly higher total rates today, as contrasted with those of a century ago, signify, for the central age groups, a different degree of institutionalization.

Analyses similar to the foregoing can be made of other counties. From Dr. Jarvis' data we find that residents of Fayette

67. Jarvis, *op. cit.*, 1866.
68. The availability of urban-rural age-specific rates in Malzberg, *op. cit.*, 1940, dictated the choice of 1930 rather than a later year.

TABLE 12

TOTAL ADMISSION RATES, ONEIDA COUNTY, NEW YORK STATE, 1843–65, AND NEW YORK STATE, 1930

	RATES	RATIOS
a. New York State, 1930	97	
b. Oneida County, 1843–65	36	a/b 2.7
c. New York 1930 rate adjusted to Oneida age distribution for 1850	73	c/b 2.0
d. New York 1930 rate adjusted to Oneida age and urban-rural distribution for 1850	53	d/b 1.5
e. New York 1930 urban-rural adjusted rate for age group 30-50	89	
f. Oneida County, age group 30-50, 1843–65	73	e/f 1.2

County, Kentucky, who had a mental hospital immediately accessible to them in Lexington, had a mean total admission rate of 59 per 100,000 general population during the years 1824–42. The residents of Davidson County, Tennessee, who had a hospital in their midst at Nashville, had a mean admission of 48 per 100,000 population for the years 1844–49. From data for later years, also provided by Dr. Jarvis, we know that these rates for the county residents declined. But for the years cited it is virtually certain, given the 19th century pattern of age-specific rates, that these counties had *higher* total admission rates in the central age groups than the states of Kentucky and Tennessee today.[69]

19th Century and Contemporary Rates for the Older Age Groups

So far our analysis has been almost exclusively confined to the central age groups, 20-50 years of age. We have noted that although the 19th century rates show parity with contempo-

69. *Report on Insanity and Idiocy in Massachusetts, by the Commission on Lunacy under Resolve of the Legislature of 1854,* House Paper No. 144 (Boston, 1855), p. 138.

rary rates in the central age groups, the contemporary rates for the oldest age groups markedly exceed those of the 19th century period. We turn to a discussion of this latter finding.

What we observe in the 19th century period appears to be an earlier stage of a phenomenon widely noted in the present century. It is now well known that a considerable proportion of the increase in recent decades in the total first admission rates in the various states of the United States is due to the remarkable increase in admissions for the mental diseases of the senium. Thus, in Illinois we find that between 1923 and 1942 admission rates for diseases of the senium increased approximately 50 percent, whereas rates for the functional psychoses or diseases of "psychogenic origin" remained unchanged.[70] Similar findings exist for Massachusetts and New York State. Since admissions in the older age groups are preponderantly for diseases of the senium (see p. 47), the difference between the 19th century and 20th century rates for the older age groups will almost necessarily have to be accounted for by admissions for the senile and arteriosclerotic psychoses. Three major possibilities present themselves: (1) that there has been a true increase in the incidence of the arteriosclerotic psychoses and that consequently the admission rates for the older age groups have risen as a result of this; (2) that there has not been a true increase in the incidence of such mental diseases, but that the tendency to hospitalize such cases has increased; (3) that the increase in rates is a result of a combination of the two foregoing factors. Morbidity and mortality data adequate to test the first hypothesis do not exist. Death certificates today increasingly tend to assign deaths involving degeneration and hemorrhage of the

70. Sommer and Harman, *op. cit.*, p. 72. By diseases of psychogenic origin is meant: dementia praecox, manic-depressive psychosis, paranoia, involutional melancholia, psychoneuroses and neuroses, and psychosis with psychopathic personality. This is the classification used by Joseph Zubin and Grace C. Sholz, "Regional Differences in the Hospitalization and Care of Patients with Mental Diseases," *Supplement No. 159 to the Public Health Reports*, U. S. Public Health Service, 1940.

brain vessels to the primary heart diseases preceding and ac-
companying these cerebral changes, and consequently do not
permit unequivocal interpretation of time series.[71] However
the possible association between hypertensive conditions and
the subsequent development of arteriosclerosis, together with
the possible increase in the former, provide at least a plausible
ground for supposing that a true increase in arteriosclerosis
may have occurred. In addition, research during the last decade has tended to disclose among normal people advanced
structural changes in the brain similar to those found in the
senile psychoses. Rothschild has further found that while vas-
cular lesions are present in all cases of psychoses with cerebral
arteriosclerosis, there appears to be little relation between the
severity of the organic and psychological pathology. The latter
seems to be more closely related to antecedent events in the patient's history.[72] Such findings lend support to the view that the
psychoses of old age are related to personality and situational
factors. This, in its turn, gives greater plausibility to the belief
that these psychoses have shown a genuine increase in incidence.

The second hypothesis is more open to test, although the
available data are far from being as satisfactory as one would
desire. If the great discrepancy between the admission rates for
the oldest age groups in the 19th and 20th centuries is in fact a
function of the lesser tendency to hospitalize such cases in the
earlier period, we would expect to find that in these age groups
the ratio of nonhospitalized to hospitalized cases is much larger
than in the earlier age groups and that this difference is greater
in the 19th century than today. We may, then, test the role of

71. Louis I. Dublin, *Health Progress 1936 to 1945: A Supplement to Twenty-Five Years of Health Progress* (Metropolitan Life Insurance Company, 1948), p. 64.

72. Cf. William Malamud, M.D., "The Psychiatric Aspects of the Problems of Old Age," *Tufts Medical Journal*, IX (1942), pp. 30-34; and David Rothschild, "Senile Psychoses and Psychoses with Cerebral Arteriosclerosis," in *Mental Disorders in Later Life*, edited by Oscar J. Kaplan (Stanford University, 1945), pp. 233-80.

hospitalization by computing ratios of nonhospitalized to hospitalized insane by age.

Adequate enumerations of nonhospitalized insane are not
available. The Bureau of the Census did provide such tabula-
tions in earlier years, although these can scarcely be presumed
adequate with respect to completeness of enumeration. However, insufficient as these censuses of the nonhospitalized insane
may be, we do not require an accurate total enumeration but
rather one in which the degree of underenumeration is the
same in all age groups. We have no guarantee that the censuses
of the insane preserve this constancy of error, but it seems almost certain that the inter-age group error is considerably less
than the total underenumeration error. From the 1880 census
of insanity, which is generally agreed to have been the most
complete of the census enumerations of the nonhospitalized
insane, we have computed for Massachusetts the ratio of noninstitutionalized to institutionalized cases by age intervals.
These ratios are

10-19	.34	50-59	.39
20-29	.50	60-69	.90
30-39	.14	70-79	2.27
40-49	.22	80-	4.10

Beginning with age 60 the ratio increases very rapidly. It
seems, then, that the low 19th century rates for the older age
groups relative to those for the central ages are, in considerable
part, a function of differential institutionalization in the various age groups.

Since the ratios include only Massachusetts cases, the numbers in the older age groups are rather small. However, the
same pattern of ratios is shown for the country as a whole on
the basis of the somewhat less adequate 1890 census by Ellen
Winston. The 1880 census does not provide the age distribution of the institutional population either for the country as a
whole or by the states, and the 1890 census provides only the

former. We have used the latter as an estimate of the Massachusetts institutional age distribution. It is essentially the same as that for resident patients in Worcester Hospital. Differences between the two distributions are such that the choice of the national distribution is conservative with respect to the particular hypothesis under test.

From the above ratios one infers that hospitalization of the insane is most apt to occur in the age group 30-39. Winston's table also supports this. This is consistent with other indications from our data bearing on the severity of the disorders found in the central age groups. The fact that 19th and 20th century rates most readily show equality in this age group is undoubtedly related to the pressure for hospitalization of this age group. This pressure eliminates in part, for the group 30-39, some of the over-all difference in 19th and 20th century facilities.[73]

Despite the progressive increase in admission rates for the older age groups, it is, of course, possible that the same age pattern of noninstitutionalized to institutionalized ratios also exists today. Adequate evidence on this point cannot, however, be marshalled. In view of the extreme rapidity of the increase during the last 20 years, it seems unlikely that the ratio of noninstitutionalized to institutionalized cases in the older age groups could be quite so high today as in the 19th century. Some indication of this is provided by a comparison between Baltimore data for 1936 and Massachusetts data for 1880. In the East Baltimore prevalence survey the median ages of nonhospitalized and hospitalized psychotics in the area were 51 and 43 years, respectively.[74] We estimate the corresponding 1880 Massachusetts median ages to be 56 and 42 years, respectively. Thus, while the Baltimore study indicates a difference

73. *A Statistical Study of Mental Disease*, University of Chicago, Ph.D. Thesis, 1930, p. 14.

74. P. Lemkau, C. Tietze, and M. Cooper, "Mental Hygiene Problems in an Urban District: Second Paper," *Mental Hygiene*, XXVI (1942), p. 107.

in median age of 8 years, we have, for the later 19th century period, a difference of 14 years. This would seem to indicate that in the contemporary period the ratio of the noninstitutionalized to institutionalized insane in the older age groups has declined.

While not excluding the very real possibility that part of the increase in admissions in the oldest age groups is due to a true increase in arteriosclerosis, the foregoing considerations strongly suggest that a major share of the increase in the age-specific rates for arteriosclerosis is due to the different hospitalization patterns for the older age groups in the 19th and 20th century periods. Landis and Page state: "In the United States there is a distinct (and growing) tendency to commit aged individuals with slight mental aberrations to mental hospitals." In Norway, where such patients are largely "boarded out" or sent to special institutions for the aged, the distribution of age-specific rates is strikingly similar to that of 19th century Massachusetts.[75]

Several factors suggest themselves as explanations for the increased hospitalization of the aged. In the first place an increase in facilities makes hospital space available for patients who normally are less dangerous or difficult to manage and whose admission in an early period of restricted accommodation would be discouraged. Such considerations might be reinforced by views on the undesirable effects of hospitalization on such cases. Thus, Dr. George Choate, superintendent of the Massachusetts state hospital at Taunton, wrote in 1860: "In these cases of dementia, occurring in old people, it may well be questioned, whether on the whole it is advisable to remove, such as are mild and manageable, to an asylum. At an age more advanced than eighty, the entire change which is made in the mode of life is exceedingly apt to operate unfavorably upon

75. Carney Landis and James D. Page, *Modern Society and Mental Disease* (New York, 1938), p. 35.

the patient, and, as there is no reasonable hope of cure, I have generally advised friends to retain them at home, unless they have exhibited traits dangerous to themselves or others." [76] The greater mobility of the population today, with the consequent separation of parents and children and the much greater difficulty of housing physically and mentally handicapped persons in small unit houses and families, probably provides greater incentive than formerly existed to institutionalize such cases. Opportunities to maintain such persons in the homes of children or other relatives would be especially limited in urban areas. In the case of the more severe and less manageable psychoses of middle life, a strong incentive to institutionalization has probably always existed whenever facilities were available. It is likely that with the growth of urbanism the incentive to institutionalize has more especially increased in the diseases of the senium. We have already noted above (p. 69) that this is apparently born out by the distribution of age-specific rates in Suffolk County. In this urban area the 19th century distribution shows a greater conformity to that of today than does the distribution for the rest of Massachusetts.

19th Century and Contemporary Rates for Ages Under Twenty

In general we have found that the parity of 19th century and contemporary rates for the central age groups 20-50 emerges

76. *Seventh Annual Report of the Trustees of the State Lunatic Hospital at Taunton,* Public Document No. 32 (Boston, 1860), p. 34. This 19th century view is in full conformity with contemporary protests against "the growing tendency to send the aged to mental institutions." This is held to be "economically unwise and therapeutically uncound" and "to interfere with the spirit of research and treatment, a spirit which is already at a very low ebb in a large proportion of our public mental hospitals." (Lawrence Kolb, "The Psychiatric Significance of Aging as a Public Health Problem," in United States Public Health Service, *Mental Health in Later Maturity,* Supplement No. 168 to the Public Health Reports (Washington, 1943), p. 14).

quite clearly from our tables. In the preceding section we have discussed the special character of the rates for the older age groups. Brief comment on the youngest age group, under 20, is now desirable. Examination of the earlier tables shows that the youngest age group does not attain parity with contemporary rates with the same consistency as the central age groups. There are, however, two comparisons in which it does attain parity. Both of these are cases where the contemporary rate is based on admissions for psychosis or "mental disorders," that is, where the rate excludes admissions without psychosis (psychopathic personality, mental deficiency, "no associated condition," etc.). Admissions without mental disorder constitute only 14 percent of contemporary first admissions for the age groups over 20, but *45 percent* of first admissions for ages under 20.[77] Consequently in analyzing 19th century and contemporary rates for the youngest age group, only rates that exclude this heavy weighting of admissions without mental disorder provide adequate comparisons. As noted above when such comparisons are made (see Tables 6 and 9) the youngest age group shows parity with contemporary rates. The comparison of Suffolk County and New York City rates (Table 11) provides additional confirmation of the parity of rates for the younger age groups. We conclude, therefore, that there is no evidence of an increase during the last century in the incidence of psychoses among persons under the age of 20, and that consequently the findings for ages 20-50 can now be stated to be true of all ages under 50.

The Effect of the Foreign-Born on Massachusetts Rates

Earlier in the report we pointed out that in making comparisons between 19th century and contemporary rates, the

77. Commonwealth of Massachusetts, *op. cit.*, 1940, p. 323.

presence of a considerable number of foreign-born in the population, and more especially the large Irish immigration of the mid-19th century, might lead one to suspect that our comparisons are invalidated by nativity differentials in our rates and populations. We assured the reader at that time (p. 52) that this was not the case and that the comparisons could be used without fear of contamination from this source. We now present the data and argument on which this conclusion rests.

The effect of nativity on our comparisons depends on two factors: (a) differences in the nativity composition of the population in the 19th century and contemporary periods; (b) differences among the nativity groups in admission rates during these two periods. If nativity groups did not differ in admission rates, it would, of course, be unnecessary to concern ourselves with differences in the nativity composition of the population in the earlier and later periods. In this case the total first admission rate would be unaffected by the nativity composition of the population. Our problem arises precisely because of the presumption that the foreign-born have higher rates than do the native-born. More particularly we are concerned with two possibilities: (a) that the excess of the foreign-born rates over native-born rates was greater in the earlier than in the later period and that the proportion of the foreign-born in the population of the early period was greater than or equal to that of the later period; (b) that the excess of foreign-born over native-born rates was the same in both periods, but that the foreign-born population constituted a greater proportion of the population of the early than of the later period. If either of these two conditions obtained, it would be possible to argue that the parity of 19th century and contemporary rates exists only by virtue of the particular character of the foreign-born rates or of the nativity composition of the population. It would follow, of course, that a parity of rates has not been established for the native-born population.

The most effective way of resolving the issues that have been raised would be to provide for both periods first admission rates that are not only age- and sex-specific but also nativity-specific. We would thus be able to compare directly the rates of both periods for foreign-born, native-born of foreign-born parents and native-born of native parents. Our data for the 19th century period do not readily permit such detailed comparisons. We do, however, have sufficient data to test whether either of the two conditions mentioned in the foregoing paragraph obtains.

Up until 1880 the six major hospitals reported the nativity of their patients. During the last five years of our 19th century period (1880–85) only the nativity of the patients' parents was reported. From these data we estimated for the central age group 20-50, for the years 1865 and 1875, the ratio of the foreign-born to the native-born rates. For 1880–85 we estimated the ratio of the foreign parentage to native parentage rates. (This is the rate ratio of foreign-born plus native-born of foreign and mixed parentage to native-born of native parentage.)

These various data together with the relevant population data may be summarized as follows: (a) The ratio of the foreign-born to the native-born rates is somewhat greater in the early period than in the contemporary period, declining in the latter part of our 19th century period to a level close to that of the contemporary period: 1865, 1.5; 1875, 1.4; 1917–33, 1.3.[78] (b) The ratio of foreign parentage to native parentage rates is *less* in the late 19th century period than in the contemporary period: 1880–85, 1.0; 1917–33, 1.3. (c) The percentage of the Massachusetts population that was foreign born was in 1840, 5; 1850, 16; 1860, 21; 1870, 24; 1880, 25; and in 1920, 29; 1930, 25. (d) The percentage of the population that was native born of foreign or mixed parentage was in 1885, 27; and in 1920, 39; 1930, 40.

78. Ratios for 1917–33 are calculated from Dayton, *op. cit.*, p. 95.

From these data we note the following observations: (a) Although the excess of the foreign-born over the native-born rates is somewhat greater in our 19th century period than in the contemporary period, this is offset by the fact that in the 19th century period the foreign-born constitute a smaller portion of the population. Toward the end of our 19th century period the proportion of the population that is foreign-born approaches very closely to that of 1917–33, but at the same time the ratios of the foreign-born and native-born rates for the two periods also approach each other closely. (b) In addition the foreign parentage group in the 19th century period is both much smaller than the same group in the contemporary period and also has a rate identical with that of the native-born; whereas in the contemporary period the foreign parentage group is larger than in the 19th century and has also a higher rate than the native parentage group. (c) From these two observations it follows that the total admission rates of the 19th century period are not "inflated" relative to those of the contemporary period by virtue of the character of the rates for foreign-born or native-born of foreign parents and by the nativity composition of the population in the two periods. It is, in fact, easier to argue that the contemporary rate is "inflated" by the foreign parentage group. In any case it is evident from the above considerations that the parity of the total rates of the 19th century and contemporary periods implies at the least a parity of the rates for the native-born of native parents.

The outcome of the foregoing analysis is further reinforced by examining the basis of the somewhat greater ratio of foreign-born to native-born rates in the mid-nineteenth century period (1.5 in 1865 as compared with 1.3 in 1917–33). This has also an independent interest inasmuch as it throws some light on the tendency in past decades toward equalization of the admission rates of different nativity groups. Although lesser control over the quality of immigration in the mid-19th century period probably played some part, the 1.5 ratio of foreign-born to native-born rates was largely due to the competitive advantages for very limited hospital space possessed by the foreign-born as compared with the native-born. The foreign-born, because of their poverty, lack of friends or family, and the desire of the communities to make them state (rather than town) wards, were more readily hospitalized than were the native-born. Their rates, then, reflect not so much a higher incidence of mental disease, but rather a higher rate of hospitalization as compared with the native-born of their own period. Contemporary testimony on this point is abundant and unequivocal. Typical is the following passage from Dr. Jarvis:

It is manifest, then, that the foreigners have enjoyed and are now enjoying the blessing of our hospitals to a greater degree than has been allowed to our own children in proportion to their numbers. . . . The foreign lunatics are mostly paupers; and as few of these have gained any local residence, they are mostly wards of the State. And if not originally paupers . . . yet, as their friends cannot or will not provide for them when deranged, they are thrown at once upon the public treasury for support, and sent to the hospital. . . . But the native lunatic is not so unhesitatingly and readily removed from his home to the public institution. . . . While the friends and overseers of the poor are generally required to meet and overcome the obstacle of increase of expense in sending their patients to a proper place for cure or custody, and therefore find strong motives for delay or entire neglect of this measure, the friends of the foreigner find a relief of a burden and a diminution of expense by adopting this measure and sending their patients to be cured. . . . The practical operation of our system is to give up our hospital accommodations for permanent residence without measure to almost the whole of the lunatic strangers, while these blessings are offered with a sparing economy to a little more than a third of our own [insane] children who are in a similar situation.[79]

We have tested these statements, using data from the prevalance survey of Massachusetts conducted by Dr. Jarvis in 1854

79. *Report on Insanity and Idiocy in Massachusetts by the Commission on Lunacy*, Public Document No. 144 (Boston, 1855), pp. 65-68.

and reported in the document just quoted. He made a very thorough prevalence count of insane patients in all classes of institutions, and a prevalence survey of the noninstitutionalized insane. The latter data were secured through questionnaires sent to 1,319 physicians (from whom returns were received from all but four!) and to a number of clergymen, and overseers of the poor. Insane were reported by name so that duplications could be removed. The degree of underenumeration is unimportant for our purpose. What is important is the relative number of foreign-born and native-born reported. This prevalence survey reveals that while the foreign-born to native-born ratio of institutionalized insane was 1.65, the ratio for both institutionalized and noninstitutionalized was .87.[80] Thus the total prevalence rate of the native-born actually exceeds that of the foreign-born. Even assuming a considerable underenumeration of the noninstitutionalized foreign-born relative to the native-born,[81] it is clear that the testimony of Dr. Jarvis and other writers of the day on the more ready institutionalization of the foreign-born is upheld. Clearly, then, the foreign-born to native-born ratios for admission rates reflect primarily different hospitalization patterns rather than markedly different rates of incidence.

Today the expansion of facilities and the diminished motives for differential hospitalization of foreign-born and native-born have given to these two groups roughly the same accessibility to hospitals. In comparing the 19th century period with

80. These ratios are based on rates calculated for the native and foreign-born populations 15 years of age and over. The difference in the age structures of these populations makes at least a rough correction of this sort imperative.

81. In order for the true ratio not to exceed 1.0 we could assume absolutely no underenumeration of the native-born uninstitutionalized insane and still tolerate a 38-percent underenumeration of the foreign-born. If, more reasonably, we assume a 20-percent underenumeration of the native-born, we can tolerate a 71-percent underenumeration of the foreign-born without the ratio rising above 1.0. Since the ratio today is somewhat greater than 1.0, we could in fact tolerate still higher levels of foreign-born underenumeration without our conclusion being affected.

today we are thus comparing a period in which the foreign-born insane had a good chance of being hospitalized and the native-born insane a poor chance of being hospitalized, with a period in which *both* nativity groups have a good chance of being hospitalized. The somewhat higher ratio of foreign-born to native-born rates in 1865 is thus not due to particularly high rates among the foreign-born, but rather to the more limited ability of the native-born to gain admission to the hospitals. It is clear that our emphasis earlier in the study on the limited hospitalization facilities of the 19th century period applies with particular force to the native-born population.

4 *SUMMARY AND CONCLUSIONS*

OUR FINDINGS may be summarized briefly as follows:

1. When appropriate comparisons are made which equate the class of patients received and the conditions affecting hospitalization of the mentally ill, age-specific first admission rates for ages under 50 are revealed to be just as high during the last half of the 19th century as they are today.

2. There has been a very marked increase in the age-specific admission rates in the older age groups. The greater part of this increase seems almost certainly to be due to an increased tendency to hospitalize persons suffering from the mental diseases of the senium. However, there is a possibility that some of the increase may be due to an actual increase in the incidence of arteriosclerosis.

3. The 19th and 20th century distributions of age-specific rates, that is, the distributions of admissions by age independent of changes in the age structure of the population, are radically different. In the 19th century there was relatively a much higher concentration of admissions in the age group 20-50; and today there is relatively a high concentration in ages over 50 and more particularly over 60. This, of course, in no way affects the results summarized in paragraph (1) above.

4. Ninteenth century admissions to mental hospitals contain a larger proportion of psychotic cases and of severe derangement than do contemporary admissions. This is in part due to the more limited facilities of that period which tended to restrict admissions to the severer cases, and to the different distribution of age-specific rates.

5. Male and female age-specific rates show a greater degree of equality in the 19th century than today. This is largely due to the differences discussed in paragraphs (3) and (4) above.

Our various discussions bearing on the validity of the findings may be summarized as follows:

1. Comparisons for the year 1885 are based almost completely on exact data involving scarcely any estimation. Wherever exact data were lacking and it was necessary to introduce estimation procedures, we have made estimates that are highly conservative with respect to the hypothesis under test. It is virtually certain that any errors in our rates for ages under 50 are errors of underenumeration.

2. In choosing data from the contemporary period with which to compare our 19th century rates, we have selected rate series that provide a severe test of the hypothesis under examination.

3. We have shown that the parity of 19th century rates with those of today is not a spurious result arising from the large foreign-born or, more especially, Irish immigration of the 19th century period.

From these more specific findings we conclude: *there has been no long-term increase during the last century in the incidence of the psychoses of early and middle life.* In view of the psychiatric character of 19th century admissions, this conclusion applies with special force to the incidence of the so-called functional or psychogenic psychoses. It is this class of mental disorders that, from the standpoint of psychiatric and social psychiatric theory, is, perhaps, of the greatest importance.

The foregoing paragraph indicates two restrictions of the conclusion that should be carefully noted: (a) the conclusion applies to secular or long-term trends; (b) it does not embrace the neuroses and psychoneuroses, nor exclude changes in the incidence of certain organic and other psychoses (e.g., paresis).

In addition to random fluctuations, admission data do show

short-term changes that coincide with marked social changes such as those incident to wars and depressions. These short-term fluctuations in admission rates may represent a true change in incidence, simply a change in the rate of hospitalization, or a combination of these two. In general, the literature takes the position that true incidence changes occur, although the evidence is often ambiguous. Almost no attempt has been made to determine to what extent the observed changes may have been produced by alterations in the hospitalization pattern. Nonetheless the experience of military psychiatry leaves no doubt that there are environmental changes and life circumstances that can have a very marked effect on the incidence of mental disorders. The extent to which such short-term changes occur in large civilian population groups, especially with respect to the more serious disorders of early and middle life, certainly deserves more intensive investigation than it has received. Here, however, our principal concern is to emphasize that our findings concerning the stability of secular trends for the psychoses is not intended in any way to minimize the importance of possible shorter-term fluctuations that have occurred in the past or may occur in the future.

The necessary restriction of the findings to the psychoses, and more especially to those of a psychogenic or functional character, raises the question whether, nonetheless, the findings have any presumptive value for statements about long-term trends in the incidence of neuroses, psychoneuroses, and character disorders. This question is all the more important since it is almost certain that the long-term incidence of these disorders cannot be subjected to adequate investigation, owing to the limitations of data bearing on the past. Possibly the use of 19th century epidemiological data might throw some light on the relative incidence of physical disorders that have strong psychogenic components, but this would undoubtedly be a very hazardous research undertaking. The extent to which findings on long-term trends in the incidence of the psychoses cast light on the neuroses depends, in part, on whether or not the incidence of these two classes of mental disorders is viewed as the product of largely the same set of causes. If one conceives of the psychosis incidence rate as being responsive to a certain total "stress vector" to which social life subjects persons, and if one believes that the component elements of this vector correspond substantially to those that affect the incidence rates of the neuroses, or are the common producers of causal factors specific to the psychoses and neuroses, then a stable psychosis rate would imply a similar stability in the incidence of the neuroses. Even though this were the case, it is likely, nonetheless, that the neurosis rate is much more sensitive to small fluctuations in the strength of the "stress vector"; consequently, small order changes in the psychosis rate which may escape detection may be accompanied by rather marked changes in the incidence of the neuroses. If, however, the immediate pathic agents and the other social factors of which they are functions are viewed as being relatively different in the case of the psychoses and the neuroses, the findings of this report would have little significance for the problem of long-term trends in the incidence of the neuroses. The weight of contemporary opinion is opposed to a completely independent aetiology of the neuroses and psychoses, but we cannot enter, in this report, into the merits of the obviously oversimplified possibilities sketched above. They have been mentioned here simply to make clear to the reader how the implications of the present report, for views on long-term trends in neurosis rates, depend on the theoretical orientation to the neuroses that the reader favors.

Contemporary writings on the theory of the psychogenic psychoses, and more especially those that have been influenced by social science, lean heavily on the presumption that these disorders are intimately related to characteristics of contemporary social existence, particularly those that are incident to the growth of "civilization." Such views are, in some cases, buttressed by the conviction that these disorders are on the increase. This general orientation toward the problem of the psychoses is not unique to our own day. The psychiatrists of the 19th century also believed that mental disease was on the increase, and they, too, appealed to the competitive character of social existence and to increased personal responsibility and freedom as an explanation. Thus Dr. Woodward, writing in 1855, says: "Here [in Massachusetts] the mind, and body too, are often worked to an extreme point of endurance. Here wealth and station are the results of well-directed efforts; and the general diffusion of intelligence among the whole people stimulates a vast 'many of them to compete successfully for these prizes. But in the contest, where so many strive, not a few break down. The results on their minds may not, perhaps, be any less disastrous, whether wealth and station are obtained or not. The true balance of the mind is disturbed by prosperity as well as adversity." [83] And Dr. Channing writes: "Modern civilization meant a departure from [a] state of automatic existence in a greater degree, and the entrance into a state of personal consciousness." [84]

Our findings have the following bearing on these and similar views expressed today, especially those that refer so freely to insecurity, competitiveness, status struggle, individuation, *anomie,* and freedom. Since they seek for an explanation of the incidence of the psychoses in these and other stresses imposed on man by his mode of social existence, we should have to conclude from our findings either (a) that, whatever may be the peculiarities of contemporary life, these stress factors as a total

83. *Twenty-second Annual Report . . . Worcester* (Boston, 1855), p. 77.

84. Walter Channing, "A Consideration of the Causes of Insanity," in *Fifth Annual Report of the State Board of Health, Lunacy and Charity, 1883* (Boston, 1884), p. 226.

conjoint force have not in fact increased during the last century, or (b) that if these factors, which are alleged to have a pathic effect, have increased, they are not as relevant for the theory of the psychoses as has been supposed. On which of these alternatives is correct, our research does not bear. Social scientists may well have an exaggerated notion of the extent to which the principal characteristics of American social life two to three generations ago differ from those of today. As we noted earlier, it is also possible that there has been a true increase in the incidence of the psychoses of the senium; possibly the tensions of contemporary existence manifest themselves more particularly in the late stages of life.

The homogeneity of 19th and 20th century rates, given what is often believed to be very significant changes in social existence, may be supposed to provide some support for theories that emphasize a genetic determination of the psychoses or the role of constitutional predispositions. While the identity of rates over a considerable period may be thought of as being consistent with such a view, we do not believe that it can be interpreted as direct evidence for it.

Theories that view the functional psychoses as resulting from repressions of basic human drives and as the consequence of trauma developing in early intimate personal and familial relationships, may possibly be thought of as being more especially consistent with our findings. These sources of psychological injury may be supposed to have remained more constant for Western society over a considerable period than the character of the total social structure itself and the motivations of adult life that it inspires. The former, to be sure, cannot be considered to be independent of changes in the latter, but it is likely that considerable changes of a social structural character are possible without involving quite so radical alterations in the nature of the early psychic traumas to which Western man is subjected.

The reader will scarcely need to be warned that the fore-going discussion has attempted only to indicate, in a very brief and oversimplified manner, the range of implications that the present research provides. A single study, such as the one re-ported here, can help to sharpen the formulation of alterna-tives, narrow the range of possible solutions to the theoretical problems at issue, and indicate promising directions for fur-ther research. Since the secular trend of admission rates has remained constant over the past 100 years, intensive research on short-term fluctuations is especially indicated. This research will first need to determine whether these fluctuations repre-sent true changes in incidence. If this is found to be so, it should then be possible to relate these rate changes to the spe-cific alterations in life circumstances associated with the pe-riods of changing rates. This would remove analysis from the level of the rather vague ascription of causation to broad social developments associated with the "growth of civilization" and lead to the analysis of the more concrete changes in social life that characterize the short-term periods under study. Only the combined and continuing research of laboratory, clinical, and social psychiatry can eventually enable us to discard those views that are inconsistent with observed fact. To this process the present report contributes the finding that, whatever may be the causal agents of the functional psychoses, they will al-most certainly have to be sought for among those life condi-tions that are equally common to American life of a hundred years ago and today.

PART II

THE CONDITIONAL EXPECTANCY
OF MENTAL DISEASE

1 *INTRODUCTION*

THE AIM of the present paper is: (1) to suggest the use of a simple expectancy measure for mental disease that is believed preferable for purposes of scientific analysis to that currently employed; (2) to present a new expectancy table (New York State data) based on the type of expectancy measure here urged; and (3) by making certain tentative estimates of the number of non-institutionalized psychotics, to extend these expectancies to include these as well as institutionalized cases. Since the emphasis of the paper is directed toward conceptual and methodological issues the problems centering around the fact that we have only estimates of the probabilities involved have been largely ignored. This seems warranted in this particular field where the numbers upon which the estimates are based are usually very large.

2 MEASURES OF INCIDENCE OF MENTAL DISEASE

THE FREQUENCY of mental disease in the United States is generally discussed in terms of the number of persons receiving treatment in hospitals for the mentally ill. Accepting, for the time being, this particular limitation or rather definition of the mentally ill, we can distinguish several different measures of the frequency of mental disease: (a) prevalence measures, the proportion of a given population group that on a given date is in a mental hospital; (b) incidence measures, the proportion of a given population that during a given year enters a mental hospital (for the first time); (c) expectancy (cumulative probability) measures, typically the chances that a person of a given age from a given population will enter a mental hospital at some time during his life or during some considerable segment of it. An expectancy measure might be considered an incidence measure in which the incidence period has been extended well beyond one year.

The present paper is concerned only with expectancy measures, although some reference will be made to the other two types. The particular relevance of an expectancy measure is little discussed. Ogburn [1] comments only that it is "equally vivid" (as compared with other measures) and Malzberg [2] speaks of it as a "refinement" in measurement. Dorn [3] indicates its

1. William F. Ogburn and Ellen Winston, "The Frequency and Probability of Insanity," *American Journal of Sociology*, XXXIV (1929), 822-831.

2. Benjamin Malzberg, "The Expectation of Mental Disease in New York State, 1920, 1930, and 1940" in American Psychopathological Association, *Trends of Mental Disease* (New York: King's Crown Press, 1945), 42-55.

3. Harold F. Dorn, "The Incidence and Future Expectancy of Mental Disease," United States Public Health Service, *Public Health Reports*, Vol. 53, No. 45 (1938), 1991-2004.

value more exactly in stating that its chief merit is to sum-
marize concisely a large number of age-specific rates. Probably
most persons have an intuitive appreciation of when a measure, expressed in terms of risk over a lifetime or some considerable segment of it, is and is not relevant. Still, it is probably
worthwhile pointing out that such a measure does not have
equal value for all morbidity conditions. Generally we would
confine the use of such a measure to a type of event which,
even though it occurs only once in a person's lifetime, is of
major consequence for the subsequent life of the individual
and for an understanding of him. Thus, in the case of the
common cold we would certainly prefer prevalence and incidence measures to lifetime probability measures. This is not
because the common cold is a "trivial" matter for our society;
this is far from being the case. It is rather because (a) individual attacks of cold, however important they may be in the
analysis of the social group, are not of great subsequent importance to the person who suffered the attack or for the study
of that individual, and because (b) individual attacks of cold
in the same individual are generally treated (correctly or in-
correctly) as "independent events." It does not follow, then,
that the social or scientific importance of a prevalence or incidence measure of a morbid condition necessarily implies the
additional desirability of an expectancy measure.

An incidence measure obtained from the proportion of persons entering a hospital during a given year for the first time is,
of course, when used as an estimate of future yearly admissions
also a probability measure. It is usually our best estimate of
the probability of admission during one year for individuals
who are members of the population under study. An expectancy (risk) measure in a similar manner states the estimated
probability that a person will be admitted to a mental hospital
over a span of years, for instance his lifetime. These measures
by confining themselves to first admissions, suggest that readmissions are to be interpreted essentially as continuations of

the same case. The incidence measure does not, however, provide an expression of frequency that illuminates the *life* position of the individual. It might be said to express the magnitude of the "social" problem, but not the magnitude of the problem for the individual, except at each specific time point separately. The problem from the standpoint of the individual comes to focus when expressed as the risk of attack during the course of a lifetime or over some extended portion of it. This does not mean that the "social" magnitude of the problem is neglected or concealed by the risk measure.

Although earlier attempts to calculate expectancy measures for mental disease exist, studies using adequate admission data for the United States first appeared in 1928. Studies by Pollock and Malzberg (1928),[4] Ogburn and Winston (1929).[5] The Metropolitan Life Insurance Company (1937),[6] Dorn (1938),[7] Jaffe and Shanas (1939),[8] Tietze (1943),[9] and Malzberg (1937, 1945)[10] appear to exhaust the list. These studies, although they exhibit some minor differences in procedure, pursue the same logic of inquiry and the expectancy measures they use have the same interpretative significance. We shall state briefly the type of answer they provide to the question of risk and compare it with an alternative method of answering this question, pointing out what is believed to be the greater scientific relevance of this alternative method.

All the studies cited proceed by taking an age cohort of a given population at a base age and computing the proportion

4. Horatio M. Pollock and Benjamin Malzberg, "Expectation of Mental Disease," *The Psychiatric Quarterly*, II (1929), 549-579.

5. Ogburn and Winston, *op. cit.*

6. Metropolitan Life Insurance Company, "The Chances of Becoming Mentally Ill," *Statistical Bulletin*, Vol. 18, No. 7 (1937), 5-8.

7. Dorn, *op. cit.*

8. A. J. Jaffe and Ethel Shanas, "Economic Differentials in the Probability of Insanity," *American Journal of Sociology*, XLIV (1939), 534-539.

9. C. Tietze, "A Note on the Incidence of Mental Disease in the State of New York," *American Journal of Psychiatry*, Vol. 100 (1943), 402-405.

10. Benjamin Malzberg, "The Expectation of Mental Disease in New York City in 1930," *Mental Hygiene*, XXI (1937), 280-290; and Malzberg (1945), *op. cit.*

of this cohort expected to enter a mental hospital at least once during the remaining years of life. The procedure followed answers the question: What is the *combined* probability of survival and of entering a mental hospital? [11] The expectation that a person in a given age cohort will enter a hospital at some time during his life is thus a function (a) of the probable length of time he will survive (as given by life tables) and (b) of the first admission rates for his group during each of the remaining years of his life expectancy. Consequently a decrease in the life expectancy of a group will lower the expectation of admission to a mental hospital since earlier mortality "rescues" members of the group from the possibility of admission. Conversely, any increase in life expectancy will increase the probability of admission since more years of life now become available during which the yearly admission probabilities apply. The expectancy measures current in the literature are thus not simply measures of the risk of mental disturbance but are measures of the risk of mental disorder *and* the risk of dying, these two components bearing an opposite relationship to the expectancy measure. This, of course, is fully realized by those who have used this measure. Ogburn, by starting his cohort at age 15, has eliminated the effect of mortality conditions prior to that age. Dorn, and Malzberg in his last study (1945), after providing detailed tables of lifetime admission expectancies for persons of each age level, supply for one age cohort (age 0) expectancies based on the mortality experience of a standard population. Like all standardized rates these do not have an absolute meaning and can only be compared with expectancies standardized on the same life tables.

Another, but more minor difficulty in the use of present expectancy tables, is that they do not provide expectancies for intermediate periods of an individual's life. One can read from such tables the expectation of admission from a specific age to

11. For convenience of reference this expectancy measure may be called a *joint* (life and admission) *expectancy measure.*

death, but not from a specific age to a specified later age. It is, however, possible to recalculate such tables in order to provide joint expectancies (based on both mortality experience and first admission rates) for specific periods of an individual's life.[12]

We wish now to raise the question as to the desirability of providing expectancies that depend to a considerable extent on mortality experience, especially in view of the fact that those who have constructed such tables are required either to warn their readers that the expectancies measure the general as well as mental health status of the population group studied, or else to undertake countermeasures such as standardization that are not entirely effective.

The choice of a measure depends, of course, on what one wants to know. The expectancy measures discussed above are fully relevant if one wants to know the probable future demand by an age cohort for mental hospital space; this requires taking life expectancies into account as well as admission rates. They are, in general, relevant where we wish to estimate the absolute number of persons who will be admitted.[13] If we are more particularly interested in knowing what effect life conditions have on the mental health of a group, it is much more relevant to ask what the first admission expectancy of a member of a certain age and population group will be *if he survives to a specified later age.* This is the "common sense" form in which one would raise the question of the *specific* risk of mental disease. We are not particularly interested in learning that our admission expectancy has been reduced because of the additional risk we run of being killed by a motor car. That some confusion exists with respect to these considerations is indi-

12. *Vide infra,* Appendix A-1.
13. In both these cases, where administrative considerations are uppermost, some account would have to be taken of the probabilities of survival through a series of recoveries and readmissions and the expected length of stay during each admission.

cated in Zubin's discussion of Dorn's expectancy rates. Zubin [14] indicates that in holding mortality constant by using a standard mortality table, Dorn has made a considerable advance over the usual method of presenting joint expectancy rates. This comment is puzzling. If one wants to know what the absolute or actual number of future admissions will be, then the joint expectancy measure must *not* be calculated on a standard mortality table. And, if one is not interested in the absolute number of future admissions and wishes to exclude mortality differences from the expectancies in making inter-group comparisons, there is simply no point in first building mortality into the rates and then turning about and removing it by standardization.

Since the expectancy measure proposed here asks what the chances are of admission for a person of a given age *if* he lives to a specified later age, we may for convenience refer to this measure as a *conditional probability or expectancy measure*. This measure does not require life tables, an additional advantage where we wish to compute expectancies for various population groups (e.g., occupational groups) for which life tables are usually not available. It uses only age-specific admission rates and is, in fact, simply equal to one minus the product of the probabilities of *not* being admitted at each age level (year) within the age interval considered. The sheer simplicity with which the conditional or one might say cumulative probability of admission over any given age interval is obtained certainly is no reason for assuming that this procedure does not give us a more useful and interpretatively significant expression of the risk of admission. It is, nonetheless, curious and not easily understandable why this procedure has been so consistently avoided in expressing the risk of mental disease. From the standpoint of scientific analysis the maximum amount of information is contained in the individual age-specific rates

14. Joseph Zubin, "Introduction," in American Psychopathological Association, *Trends of Mental Disease* (New York: King's Crown Press, 1945), 7-8.

themselves. But if one wishes an effective summary of a considerable number of age-specific rates and to use these as an expression of the individual's risk of admission, then the procedure suggested here is, we believe, decidedly preferable.[15]

Although we can easily obtain the conditional probability of admission over any age range, from the age specific rates, other measures of the risk of admission may be constructed which likewise are independent of competing morbidity or mortality conditions. Among these alternatives one that readily suggests itself is the measure obtained by summing the age specific admission rates. The sum of these probabilities can exceed one and it does not, as is easily seen from elementary probability theorems, represent the conditional probability of admission or probability risk of mental disease. Nonetheless it has many of the properties one demands of a measure. The sum is an increasing function of the age specific rates and represents a one to one transformation of the conditional probability measure suggested above. We have investigated the numerical properties of the summation measure and find that for age specific probabilities of admission of the order of magnitude prevailing in mental disease data the two measures are numerically almost identical.

It is desirable to present these different expectancy measures in a precise notational form. Appendix A-1 of this paper gives the *joint expectancy measure* used by Ogburn, Pollock and Malzberg and others in a form somewhat modified for easier comparison with our own measure. A-2 states the *conditional expectancy measure* discussed above. In non-notational form the difference between A-1 and A-2 may be expressed as fol-

15. In one of his recent books Neyman has devoted a section to a problem of this general type, calling it the problem of competing risks. He also concludes that "the concept which suggests itself is that of the long run relative frequency of the given risk if it were observed in artificial conditions where all other risks were eliminated." For a very excellent and full exposition of the conceptual probability problems involved we refer the reader to pp. 69-95 of J. Neyman, *First Course in Probability and Statistics*, Henry Holt and Co., New York, 1950.

lows: A-1 states the (joint) probability that a person at age X will survive and be admitted to a hospital. A-2, the conditional expectancy measure, on the other hand, states the probability that a person of a specified age will be admitted to a hospital by a specified later age if he lives to that age. Appendix A-3 gives the obvious expression for the summation measure and its relation to the conditional expectancy measure.

Before presenting the conditional expectancies that we have computed for New York State, it is desirable to indicate two refinements that may be applied to the expectancy measures we have considered.

It is axiomatic that a risk rate be computed to a population base that includes only those who are exposed to the risk under analysis. In calculating the first admission rates that enter into the two expectancy measures discussed above, the denominator should properly be the "exposed population" in the age group concerned rather than the total population. The population base would thus require, at the very least, the elimination of those persons who are already in a mental hospital and those who have been in a mental hospital and have since been discharged and are still alive. These persons are no longer exposed to the risk of first admission.[16] Since the probable size of the group to be eliminated from the population base and its effect on age-specific admission rates do not appear to have been dealt with elsewhere, we made some rough calculations for New York State for the year 1940. These calculations depend on various assumptions about the life tables of the hospitalized population and the age distribution and life tables of the previously hospitalized but now discharged populations. These calculations suggest that for the age groups between 55 and 75 the proportion of the total population requiring elimination to arrive at the exposed population is approximately 3 to 4 per-

---

16. Of course the reduction of the total population to the exposed population has little point unless the enumeration of the total population is itself very accurate or, more especially, has been corrected for underenumeration.

cent. For the younger age groups it is considerably smaller (e.g., 1 percent for the age group 35-44). A small percentage error in the population base produces an error of virtually the same percent in the first admission rate calculated on this population base. In preparing the conditional expectancy tables given on pages 114-115 we have not made this correction for the age-specific first admission rates on which the table is based. For the use of those who may wish to make this correction for particular population groups in which the error may be more appreciable,[17] we have provided in Appendix B a brief statement of the method of calculating the correction.

A second refinement in the construction of expectancy tables can be introduced by the use of generation rather than current life tables.[18] The joint expectancy rates now available are based on current life tables which assume that the age-specific mortality rates currently in effect will still be operative during the future years through which the age cohort will pass. As the cohort grows older, however, life expectancy may alter. Death rates current today are applied to a zero age cohort which will in fact be subject, in considerable measure, to the death rates prevailing between now and the next 90 or 100 years. The use of generation life tables involves making assumptions about future trends in the mortality rate; this, perhaps, may be considered undesirable. However the use of current life tables equally involves an assumption, namely that the age-specific death rates will be constant during the coming years. The decision to use one table rather than another is a matter of how much error is likely to be introduced by the assumption of constant death rates.

The decision whether to use current or generation life tables arises only in connection with the joint expectancy rates used by previous writers since the conditional expectancy measure

17. This, for instance, would be true of the Negro population.
18. For a discussion of current and generation life tables see Louis I. Dublin and Mortimer Spiegelman, "Current Versus Generation Life Tables," *Human Biology*, 13 (1941), 439-458.

suggested in this paper does not use life tables. However, both for the joint expectancy measure and the one urged in this paper a similar problem arises with respect to the age-specific admission rates used in the calculation of the expectancies. Here, too, it is possible to assume that a given age cohort will be subject during future years to the admission rates currently in effect or to admission rates which are themselves subject to change during the years to which the expectancies are intended to apply. The estimation of future age-specific admission rates may be more hazardous than the same procedure in the case of life tables. In any event the age-specific first admission rates, for states with relatively well developed hospital systems, have not in the last decades undergone much change in the young and middle age groups. Appreciable increases are observable in the admission rates of the older age groups. We have not attempted a forecast of changes in the age-specific first admission rates for future years and consequently the tables presented in the next section of the paper are based on established rates. This probably leads to some underestimation of the future expectancy of admission for ages above 65.

Calculations of risk based on hospital admission data allocate patients to the age group to which they belong at the time of first admission. However, persons who enter mental hospitals have often had the actual onset of their disease well in advance of their entry into the hospital. Risk curves based on admission data must therefore be understood to provide the risk up to a given age of admission to a hospital and not the risk of onset of a mental disease by that age. This consideration applies to the population that ultimately becomes hospitalized and is quite independent of the additional consideration that not all mentally ill people become hospitalized. We hope in the future to be able to show in what way conclusions about the relative frequency of mental disease in different age groups are affected by the use of age-at-onset data.

3 CONDITIONAL EXPECTANCY RATES FOR NEW YORK STATE

TABLES 1 AND 2 present the conditional expectation that men and women in New York State will be admitted to a mental hospital at some time during the years specified in the two margins of the tables. These tables have been prepared on the basis of New York State age-specific admission rates for 1940.[19] Admission rates for later years are, of course, available but 1940 data were used, first, because of the special character of admission rates during the war years and, secondly, because of a desire to make the conditional expectancy rates presented here comparable with the 1940 joint expectancy rates provided by Malzberg. The admission rates used for these tables are identical with those used by Malzberg and this permits a better comparison of the difference in expectancy measures provided by the currently used methods of computation and those suggested in this paper.

Tables 1 and 2 are to be read as providing the chances out of 100 that a person (in New York State) of any given age (read from the left margin of the table) will be admitted to a mental hospital by the time he reaches any later age (given by the top margin). Expectancies beginning with any age between 0 and 10 have been presented in the first line of each table; so few admissions occur during these early years that expectancies beginning at any age between birth and age 10 are virtually identical.

It will be recalled that these tables present the expectation that a person will be admitted by a given age *provided* that he

19. Benjamin Malzberg, *op. cit.*, *Trends of Mental Disease*, pp. 42-55.

TABLE 1

CONDITIONAL EXPECTANCY (CHANCES IN 100) OF FIRST ADMISSION TO A MENTAL HOSPITAL BETWEEN ANY TWO AGES: MALES, NEW YORK STATE, 1940.

INITIAL AGE	TERMINAL AGE															
	15	20	25	30	35	40	45	50	55	60	65	70	75	80	85	90
0–10*	.11	.43	.92	1.49	2.10	2.76	3.44	4.16	4.93	5.79	6.83	8.17	10.07	12.76	16.20	20.12
15		.32	.82	1.39	2.00	2.66	3.34	4.06	4.83	5.69	6.73	8.08	9.97	12.66	16.11	20.04
20			.50	1.07	1.69	2.35	3.03	3.75	4.53	5.38	6.43	7.78	9.68	12.38	15.84	19.78
25				.57	1.19	1.86	2.54	3.26	4.05	4.91	5.96	7.32	9.23	11.94	15.42	19.38
30					.62	1.29	1.98	2.71	3.49	4.36	5.42	6.78	8.70	11.44	14.93	18.91
35						.67	1.36	2.10	2.89	3.76	4.83	6.20	8.13	10.88	14.40	18.40
40							.70	1.44	2.23	3.11	4.18	5.57	7.51	10.28	13.82	17.85
45								.74	1.55	2.43	3.51	4.90	6.86	9.65	13.22	17.28
50									.81	1.70	2.79	4.19	6.16	8.97	12.57	16.66
55										.90	2.00	3.41	5.40	8.23	11.85	15.98
60											1.11	2.54	4.54	7.40	11.06	15.22
65												1.44	3.47	6.36	10.06	14.27
70													2.06	4.99	8.74	13.01
75														2.99	6.82	11.18
80															3.95	8.44
85																4.68

* See Text.

TABLE 2

CONDITIONAL EXPECTANCY (CHANCES IN 100) OF FIRST ADMISSION TO A MENTAL HOSPITAL BETWEEN ANY TWO AGES: FEMALES, NEW YORK STATE, 1940

INITIAL AGE	TERMINAL AGE															
	15	20	25	30	35	40	45	50	55	60	65	70	75	80	85	90
0–10*	.09	.34	.75	1.26	1.82	2.41	3.03	3.69	4.38	5.11	6.00	7.15	8.78	11.14	14.27	18.08
15		.25	.67	1.17	1.73	2.32	2.95	3.60	4.29	5.03	5.92	7.07	8.70	11.07	14.19	18.01
20			.41	.92	1.48	2.07	2.70	3.36	4.05	4.79	5.68	6.83	8.46	10.84	13.97	17.80
25				.51	1.07	1.67	2.29	2.96	3.65	4.39	5.29	6.44	8.08	10.47	13.61	17.46
30					.56	1.16	1.79	2.46	3.16	3.90	4.80	5.96	7.61	10.01	13.17	17.03
35						.61	1.24	1.91	2.61	3.36	4.26	5.43	7.09	9.50	12.68	16.56
40							.64	1.31	2.02	2.77	3.68	4.86	6.52	8.95	12.15	16.06
45								.68	1.39	2.15	3.06	4.25	5.92	8.37	11.58	15.52
50									.72	1.48	2.40	3.59	5.28	7.74	10.98	14.94
55										.77	1.70	2.90	4.60	7.08	10.34	14.33
60											.94	2.14	3.86	6.35	9.64	13.66
65												1.22	2.95	5.47	8.79	12.85
70													1.75	4.30	7.66	11.77
75														2.59	6.02	10.20
80															3.51	7.81
85																4.45

* See Text.

lives to that age. Consequently in comparing the expectancy figures provided by these tables with those given by Malzberg striking differences emerge, particularly with respect to the probability of admission at the older ages. Thus our table shows that in New York State a male who survives from birth to the age of 90 has 1 chance in 5 of being admitted to a mental hospital by that age. The expectancy tables of Malzberg, Ogburn, Dorn and others do not permit the reading of an expectancy figure for a group with a specific terminal age. However calculating the combined expectancy of survival and admission (by the method of Appendix A-1) we find that the joint expectancy of admission is approximately 1 chance in 25. This much lower expectancy by age 90 is, of course, due to the fact that the chances of survival to this age are relatively small and since this is incorporated in the joint expectancy computation the chances of admission by this age are likewise reduced. Our own figure of 1 chance in 5 for admission by the age of 90 expresses, on the contrary, the chances of admission provided that such survival occurs. Similarly our table for males shows that the chances of admission to a mental hospital for a person who lives from birth to the age of 65 is 1 in 15. This compares with a figure of 1 in 20 by the method which gives the combined probability of surviving to the age of 65 and being admitted by that age. One further example: Table 1 shows that a male in New York State who has lived to the age of 65 without any prior admission to a mental hospital has approximately 1 chance in 16 of being admitted if he survives 15 more years to the age of 80. Computing the combined probability of survival from the age of 65 to 80 and the probability of admission during this period we find that the expectation of admission on this basis is 1 chance in 30.

The advantage of our conditional expectancies which exclude the influence of mortality conditions emerges clearly in comparing the ratios of our male-female expectancies with

those provided by Malzberg. Malzberg's female expectancy figures are almost as high as the expectancies for males for ages
up to 65, and are given as higher than males for ages above 65.
The reason for this is, of course, that the method of joint
probability is influenced by the longer life expectancy of females; longer life provides a greater number of years over
which admission may take place and thus places the female expectancy rate on a parity with or in excess of the male rate.
Since our expectancy figures eliminate the effect of differential
mortality conditions, the female expectancies are for all age
groups considerably less than those for males. This expresses
the fact that for men and women who live the same length of
time, the men have a greater expectancy of admission to a mental hospital than the women.

It is apparent from Tables 1 and 2 that the probability of
admission to a mental hospital increases rapidly in the older
age groups. By the age of 65 the chances of admission for a
male surviving to this age are approximately 1 in 15; for the
group surviving to the age of 75 this increases to 1 in 10; and
for the group surviving to the age of 85 to 1 chance in 6. We
have not included in the table expectancy figures for ages over
90 since owing to the small number of admissions above this
age the stability of such figures is too small.[20] These expectancy
figures point up rather sharply the dilemma involved in an increased extension of life that does not, however, signify a freedom from the hazards of degenerative diseases which even
though they may not cut off life nonetheless often debar the
individual from a useful life and agreeable life conditions.[21]

20. However it may be mentioned that taking the available rates for the ages
above 90 the chance of admission for a person who lives to the age of 100 turns
out to be approximately 1 in 3.
21. The problem in the older age groups is, however, not simply one of man-
aging or possibly combating the inroads of the degenerative processes associated
with senescence, since there appears to be good reason to believe that physical
deterioration and susceptibility to mental collapse during the period of physical
deterioration are at least in part psychogenically determined.

In view of the fact that average life expectancy is now approximately 67 years [22] and that many adults can look forward to survival to this age, it is apparent that the risk of admission constitutes a very major hazard of contemporary existence.

Although the expectancies are of a somewhat different order of magnitude in the younger age groups, they are by no means inconsequential. Thus we find that between the ages of 15 and 45 the chances of admission to a mental hospital are approximately 1 in 30 for males who survive to the latter age. By the age of 65, as we have noted above, the expectation increases to 1 in 15.

It should be pointed out more explicitly that the expectancies that we have been discussing are based on first admission rates for New York State. These rates are among the highest state rates in the country, but there is no reason to believe that the rates of other urban states would be markedly lower were their hospital facilities more comparable to those provided by New York State. In the more rural sections of the country even comparable hospital facilities might not produce a rate equivalent to that of New York State. This, however, would probably be due to the lesser inclination of persons living in rural areas to send their mentally ill to mental hospitals; partly, no doubt, this is due to the greater ease with which care can be given to the mentally ill in rural surroundings, and partly to a diminished consciousness of the facilities available. There is reason to believe, although we cannot discuss the evidence for this here, that the incidence of psychoses is quite as high in rural as in urban areas. In general, then, we may take the New York expectancy figures as representing the chances of admission to a mental hospital where adequate facilities are available and where no strong disinclination exists to hospitalize persons who are admissible.

22. Metropolitan Life Insurance Company, *Statistical Bulletin*, Vol. 29, No. 11 (November 1948), p. 5.

4 PROVISIONAL ADJUSTMENT OF CONDITIONAL EXPECTANCY RATES BASED ON HOSPITAL DATA

THE EXPECTANCY RATES so far discussed are based on admissions to mental hospitals. If we ask what the expectancy is of a mental disorder sufficiently severe to justify admission to a mental hospital, we are immediately plunged into the realm of conjecture. Data exist which suggest that the ratio of non-hospitalized to hospitalized psychotics is sufficiently large to make the use of mental hospital statistics of perhaps limited value as an expression of the true prevalence and incidence rates of severe mental disorder. The East Baltimore survey of 1936 showed that in this section of Baltimore for every 4 persons from the area currently hospitalized for mental diseases there was one person outside of the hospital, never previously admitted, described as a psychotic.[23] Since the cases reported by this survey were uncovered through the records of various private and public agencies, we can almost certainly assume that an additional number of unhospitalized psychotics were living in the district at that time. A 1938 survey of Williamson County, Tennessee, revealed close to one person diagnosed as psychotic who had never been admitted to a mental hospital for every one person currently in a mental hospital admitted from this county.[24] The strikingly higher rate of "outside cases" in the

23. Paul Lemkau, Christopher Tietze, and Marcia Cooper, "Mental Hygiene Problems in an Urban District: Second Paper," *Mental Hygiene*, XXVI (1942), 100-119.

24. W. F. Roth and F. H. Luton, "The Mental Health Program in Tennessee," *American Journal of Psychiatry*, 99 (1943), 662-675.

Tennessee survey is probably due to a combination of two factors. The Tennessee survey was more thoroughgoing in its case-finding techniques. It was based on information provided by physicians, nurses, teachers, ministers, and others, and also on the work of field investigators who mingled with the people of the communities in the county. A second factor that probably accounts for the higher outside rate in Tennessee is its rural character and the associated lower rate of hospitalization. Despite the relative thoroughness of the case-finding procedures in the Tennessee county, it should be added that when three areas within the county were selected for an especially intensive house-to-house survey, the prevalence rate for these areas turned out to be about twice the rate for the remainder of the county.

Further evidence on the proportion of psychotics not hospitalized is provided by Selective Service data of World War II. These data, for a variety of reasons which we need not enter into here, are extremely difficult to analyze adequately in their presently available form. However, we have made tentative estimates of the ratio of males in the age group 18-37 with a diagnosis of psychosis to those of this age group who are on the books of mental hospitals. This calculation takes into account that a number of the persons rejected for psychosis were rejected simply on the basis of a previous hospitalization record and consequently cannot be counted as active cases in a prevalence count. We also excluded some cases from the Selective Service psychosis categories that appear to be pre-psychotic and severe psychoneuroses. Population selection due to enlistments and deferments was also taken into account although no very precise adjustment for this was made. In this manner we estimate the ratio of outside to hospitalized cases to be approximately .5 for New York State. This, of course, provides only a corrected prevalence rate and other studies of the authors suggest that in similar cases the appropriate adjustment in age-specific incidence rates varies from age group to age group and is on the whole rather small except for the very youngest age groups. It will be noted that the ratio of psychotics outside of hospitals to those inside of hospitals for the Selective Service data falls in between the figures for Baltimore and Tennessee. In view of the fact that New York State is highly urban, the Selective Service estimate seems rather plausible since one anticipates a higher proportion of unhospitalized cases in rural areas.

The East Baltimore survey showed that the non-hospitalized psychotics were somewhat older than those that had been hospitalized. It would appear, then, that we may assume that the proportion of unhospitalized male cases is at least as high in the older age groups as in those age groups subject to Selective Service examination. If we make this assumption our other work indicates that we would have to increase the expectancy rates of Table 1 by factors varying from 100 percent for the 15-19 age group to 5 percent for the middle age groups in order to reach an expectancy figure stating the probability of a severe mental disorder. This would mean that the conditional expectancy for males in New York State of being admitted to a mental hospital by the age of 75 of 1 in 10 would now have to be translated into a chance of 1 in 9 of a major mental disorder by the age of 75; a chance of 1 in 13 by age 65; a chance of 1 in 25 by age 45; and a chance of 1 in 74 by age 25.

There is now increasing interest in the provision of more accurate estimates of the frequency of psychotic conditions that are not hospitalized. In the meantime, it is apparent that current estimates (such as those we have made above) are generally treated as minimal estimates. However, the shift from hospitalized to non-hospitalized cases involves to an undetermined extent a shift in diagnostic classes. Consequently for the time being it is not advisable freely to assume that the number of cases of a type equivalent to those admitted to mental hospitals is, in a state such as New York with well developed hospital facilities, much in excess of the estimates now available. That the estimates may be low is entirely possible, but without fuller psychiatric examination of suspected cases it would be dangerous to assume that this must necessarily be the case.

APPENDICES TO PART II

THE FOLLOWING appendices contain simple, but systematic, formulations of the various expectancy measures discussed in the main body of the text. The resulting formulae constitute the basis for the calculation of the expectancy measures when requisite data are available. In addition to the expectancy measures a correction factor for the computation of age-specific first admission rates is discussed.

APPENDIX A: *Expectancy Measures*

The Basic Model. The basic model of the underlying process which will be used to formulate the several expectancy measures of the risk of insanity is the simplest one possible. In this model there are only three possible states of the world for an individual to be a member of: state 1, alive and sane (i.e., never a patient of a mental institution; as mentioned in the text this is merely a particular, arbitrary definition of sanity); state 2, insane (conversely this is defined as having been or currently being a patient in a mental institution); and state 3, death. These particular choices for the definitions of the three states may at first appear somehow unreal but a little reflection will reveal how convenient they are for the discussion of the first admission process over time. Let

$$\lambda_i = \text{probability of death at age } i$$

$$\xi_i = \text{probability of admission to a mental institution at age } i \text{ if never admitted before}$$

then P_X the probability of surviving to age X without ever having been admitted to a mental institution is equal to

$$\prod_{i=1}^{X-1} (1 - \xi_i - \lambda_i) = P_X.$$

A-1 *The Joint Expectancy Measure*

The joint expectancy measure of the Pollock-Malzberg type is really equivalent to the probability of being admitted to a mental institution at least once in one's lifetime. It is easily seen that this probability is equal to

$$\sum_{n=1}^{D} P_n \xi_n$$

where D is the least integer n such that $P_n = O$ and, of course, $P_{n+i} = O$ for $i > O$. For initial ages other than birth the correct expression is

$$\sum_{n=X}^{D} \frac{P_n \xi_n}{P_X}.$$

This is the probability of admission to a mental institution at least once in the remainder of one's lifetime given that one has survived sane until age X. Similarly when a joint expectancy measure which provides for a specific terminal age rather than D is required, the correct expression is

$$\sum_{n=X}^{r-1} \frac{P_n \xi_n}{P_X}.$$

A-2 *The Conditional Expectancy Measure*

The conditional expectancy measure which we have proposed in the text and on which tables 1 and 2 are based, for initial age X and terminal age Y, is

$$1 - \prod_{n=X}^{r-1} (1 - \xi_n).$$

This measures the specific risk of admission to mental institutions given survival is certain from age X to age Y.

A-3 *The Summation Expectancy Measure*

Using the above notation the summation measure of risk is

$$\sum_{n=X}^{r-1} \xi_n$$

where X and Y are the initial and terminal ages respectively of the age interval with which we are concerned. As pointed out in the text unlike the other two expectancy measures this is not the probability of any event, at least not of any interesting event. When the age specific probabilities are very small, as is the case in mental disease data where for ages 10-90, $.0001 < \xi_n < .01$, a very good approximation of $1 - \xi_n$ is $e^{-\xi_n}$. This can be seen from the first few terms of the Taylor's series expansion of $e^{-\xi_n}$ since the error in the above approximation is less than $\xi^2_n/2$. Thus

$$\sum_{n=X}^{Y-1} \xi_n \sim \left[1 - e^{-\sum_{n=X}^{Y-1} \xi_n} \right] \sim \left[1 - \prod_{n=X}^{Y-1} (1 - \xi_n) \right].$$

In our data the maximum error in this approximation is on the order of two percent and for Y less than or equal to 80 the error is nearer to one-half of one percent.

APPENDIX B: *A Correction Factor for the Computation of Age-Specific Rates*

In principle, what is to be computed is the number of people, alive, at given date of a given age group who have at one time been first admissions to a mental hospital. For, say, the 50-year age group in 1940, this is easily seen to be equal to the sum of the first admissions of age 49 in 1939 who have survived to 1940, the first admissions of age 48 in 1938 who have survived to 1940, and so on. This may be expressed as follows. Let

$A_{(Y-i)(X-i)}$ = the number of first admissions in the year $(X - i)$ of age $(Y - i)$

and

$P_{(Y-i)(X-i)}$ = the probability of surviving the year X if first admitted to a mental hospital in year $(X-i)$ at age $(Y-i)$.

Then the number alive of age Y in year X who have been admitted at least once to a mental hospital is equal to

$$\sum_{i=1}^{r} A_{(Y-i)(X-i)} \ P_{(Y-i)(X-i)}.$$

Thus, given the proper life tables and the number of admissions in the various age groups for a sufficient number of past years, we can produce good estimates of the required population correction.